Contents

Introduction

The **Mighty Multiples Times Table Challenge** provides a fun, interactive and practical way of learning the times tables.

This unique approach is:

Fun
The scheme contains enjoyable activities which engage children in their learning.

Interactive
It provides a visual, auditory and kinaesthetic approach to learning the times tables which will appeal to all children, whatever their learning style:

- **Visual** – Each times table is linked to a sporting character and there are visual grouping sheets, number fans, 144 grids and bingo games
- **Auditory** – Pupils can listen and sing along to the character's songs and poems on the CDs
- **Kinaesthetic** – Activities to enable you to jump and leap your way through the times tables! Links to PE and major sporting events!

Practical, tried and tested
This tried and tested method really works. Our trial schools recorded a significant improvement in children's understanding of the tables. We measured children's times table knowledge for the age appropriate level and, at the end of the trial, 84 percent could recite tables and almost all children could solve word problems relating to applying times table knowledge. The most marked improvement was in attitude towards the times tables. At the beginning 86 percent said they hated times tables and thought they were boring but, at the end of the year, 90 percent said they loved the Mighty Multiples!

The **Mighty Multiples Times Table Challenge** provides:

A fresh. new integrated approach
The scheme provides lots of practical multiplication and division activities so children gain full understanding. Children learn to apply their times table knowledge to word problems and everyday life situations.

In-built motivational rewards, badges and certificates
How long will it take for your pupils to achieve their Bronze, Silver, Gold and Platinum Awards? (See page 21.)

Everything you need
The book and 2CDs pack contains everything you need, from group games, number fans and visual grouping activities to songs, poems and assessment activities. All the songs and poems are recorded on CD1, along with instrumental versions of the songs on CD2.

Suggestions for starting a Mighty Multiples Club
A great way to raise the profile of maths across the school (see page 20).

Links to home
Tip sheets for parents for use at the park, while shopping and on the way to school to help make times tables relevant to everyday life (see pages 28-32).

Using the scheme in your school

The Mighty Multiples Times Table Challenge is a whole school scheme, starting at Reception and continuing to Year 6. It teaches the times tables and consolidates number bond knowledge. The scheme is designed to teach the times tables by developing a clear understanding of how to use and apply this knowledge to division and word problems and not simply learning by rote.

Each times table or number bond is linked to a sporting character and each character has its own corresponding songs, poems and tips to help the children learn. The scheme is designed to be taught practically and should always remain fun.

The whole scheme is split into awards and follows a natural progression of skills. It starts with a bronze award, which covers number bonds and number stories to 20, up to a platinum award, covering the 11 and 12 times tables.

Included in the scheme are complete assessment materials, in order to monitor whole class and individual achievements.

When should we start the scheme?
The scheme is best started at the beginning of a new term. This will be a long enough stretch to measure progression.

How often should we use the scheme?
This is entirely up to your school. The scheme is designed to be flexible. You may choose to use it daily, weekly or just to fill the occasional spare moments in the week.

Should everyone take part?
Yes! The idea of the scheme is that the characters are so well known and the achievement of an award is so well recognized that children are proud and self-motivated to take part.

When should we give awards?
We would ideally recommend that these are given out in whole school assemblies, in order to recognize achievement within the school community.

How do we know when to assess?
All teachers know their own pupils best. We recommend that you do not assess a child until you are sure they stand a good chance of passing the assessment as the testing is so thorough. Provided are morale boosting 'In between' certificates to acknowledge the hard work and effort put into learning (see pages 24–25).

Assessment sheets

Assessment sheets are provided at the end of each number bond or times table. There is also a whole class tracking sheet to record individual's progress (page 27), which can be used in transition when children move to the next academic year. The child record sheet contains pictures of all the characters and details of what they should be learning to achieve each award (page 26). When they complete a table assessment, they can colour in the corresponding character on their individual sheet.

What do we send home?

Each table has its own sheet to take home, including the table to learn and activities and tips to help do so. All tips are practical and fun! Parents should be encouraged to keep the fun element of this learning and not to make children learn the tables by rote.

It might be advisable to invite parents in for an open evening to explain the scheme and answer any questions, so that parents have a thorough understanding of what you are trying to achieve with their help.

Does every child have to start at the beginning of the scheme?

Yes! Although some children may be more advanced than number bonds and the tables necessary for the lower awards, it is important that every child starts at the same point. The more able children can be assessed immediately on the lower awards and achieve them quickly. It not only consolidates each child's knowledge but is motivating both for that child and other children to see the reality of people achieving awards.

Meet the characters

100 metre Peter
Number stories

200 metre Travis
Number bonds

400 metre Sinitta
2 times table

High Jump Heather
3 times table

Freestyle Freda
4 times table

Javelin John
5 times table

Backstroke Brenda
6 times table

Cycling Susie
7 times table

Triple Jump Tracey
8 times table

Shot Put Tony
9 times table

Long Jump Jim
10 times table

1000 metre Glenda
11 times table

Aerobic Alan
12 times table

High Dive Clive
Mixed tables, 1

Triathlon Saffron
Mixed tables, 2

Mighty Multiples poem

So, you hate times tables? You think they're boring?
Fear not, my friends, just wait and see –
These Mighty Multiples shall stop you snoring!
With our help and expertise, you'll find learning tables such a breeze.

Now, with no more ado, let's introduce our number friends to you:
Sprinting through stories and bonding with numbers,
Are trusty old Travis and plucky young Peter,
They'll be right there alongside you at every metre.

Our expert in 4s is Freestyle Freda: you never know when you might
    need her.
But who shall help with number 5?
Oh PHEW! – it's Javelin John and High Dive Clive!

And then there's Triathlon Saffron and Susie and Brenda,
And when it gets tough, Aerobic Alan and Glenda.
High Jump Heather looks after times table 3,
And Sinitta won't let anyone beat her – you'll see.

Shot Put Tony turns nasty 9s nice,
And Jim will teach you the 10s in a trice!
Susie and Tracey with the dreaded 7s and 8s...
Nothing to worry about though, you'll all soon be mates!

And just think, by learning those tables both outside and in,
You're giving yourself the best possible chance of a win!
Imagine, learning times tables outdoors?!
You'll soon collect that certificate to thunderous applause.

Mighty teaching tips

Can you spot any patterns?

◆ Sometimes it helps people if they recognize patterns when learning their times tables.

◆ Use your mighty multiple times table 144 grid (page 175) to notice any patterns.

◆ Here are a few you may notice:

2 times table
They are always even numbers!

5 times table
They always end in a 5 or a 0: 5, 10, 15, 20, 25, 30, 35, 40, 45, 50 etc. They always alternate too!

10 times table
The beginning of the answer is always in the question!

$1 \times 10 = 10$
$2 \times 10 = 20$
$3 \times 10 = 30$

9 times table
The nines have a very noticeable pattern:

09
18
27
36
45

If you look at the pattern you, will notice that each time you add 10 to the tens column, you take 1 from units colomun!

Make learning times tables fun!

◆ Count in your table as you line up.

◆ Answer the register in your tables.

◆ Walk to your destination singing a table and doing an action, eg for Freestyle Freda, sing your 4s and pretend to swim to assembly!

◆ Play number bingo. Give the class a times table question, eg 4 x 4. They can tick 16 if they have it and know the answer!

◆ Decide which character everyone is. Put spots on the floor with numbers on. When they hear a signal, eg a drum, children jump onto a number that is in their times table. Take one spot away each time, until you have a winner!

◆ Take a large die outside, roll it. Pupils times that number by their character's number! Whatever the answer, pupils jump on the spot that many times or run around the playground etc.

◆ Make the half time snacks out of play dough, then divide them up between different numbers of characters.

- Scrunch up paper balls to look like shot puts. Throw them into the bin counting in 2s. Or throw them into hoops; number the hoops and times your number by the number on the hoop!

- Scatter numbers upside down on the floor. Sit the children around the numbers. Give two children a times table question. They have to race to find the answer!

- Splat! Write down the factors and multiples of the times table you are practising on a piece of paper. Roll a die 5 times. Use the numbers rolled to try to make your factors and multiples.

- Build a tower with blocks counting in 2s or 3s etc.

5-minute mighty tips
- Use the track on page 22 to do a quick challenge. Pupils write their number in the middle. How many times can they go around the track in 5 minutes?

- Ask pupils to recite their tables backwards and sit down. Can everyone in the class sit down before the timer stops?

- Sing a Mighty Multiple song!

- Get every child to write a word problem involving a given table. Swap it with a partner and answer each other's question.

- Ask a child to come to the front to be the quiz master. They get to shout out the question and the children have to put up their hands to answer. If the child gets it correct, they swap places.

- Give every child a Mighty Multiple number fan. Ask quick fire questions. They must show you the answer on their number fan, allowing you to quickly assess who is sure and who is unsure.

- Call out a number, eg 15. The class have to do an action that represents a character that could have 15 as a multiple. So, for this for example, they may jump high like High Jump Heather (3s) or perhaps throw a javelin like Javelin John (5s)!

- Do the action of a character whilst quickly reciting their table! For example cycle on the spot quickly whilst reciting the 7 times table like Cycling Susie.

10 mighty minutes to fill?
- Play trigger shooter. Ask one child to come to the front and make a shooter with their hands. Ask them times table questions to answer. They keep going until somebody on the carpet has put their hand up quicker to answer the question (and gets it correct) before the child at the front has fired the answer.

- Throw a die. Whatever it lands on the children have to times by the number you put on the board. Keep going around the circle. See how many questions the class can answer in 10 minutes!

◆ Divide the class into four groups. Each group has five minutes to go away and write five questions. They then swap questions, so that every group has a different set of questions to the ones they wrote. Which group can complete the questions quickest? This will prepare children well for assessments and get them thinking of questions too.

Have you 15 mighty minutes to fill?

◆ Play times table bingo. Give the children each a blank bingo grid (see pages 176-177), they must fill it in with 6/8 numbers that are a multiple of their given number. You then call out questions and if they have the answer they can either cover with a counter or cross out! The winner is the first to cover all their numbers, but instead of 'bingo' they must shout 'I am ...' whichever character your times table is covering, eg for the 10 times table, they would shout 'I am Long Jump Jim.'

◆ Split the class in half. Give each team a table, for example 4 and 6. They must challenge the other team one at a time to answer a question about that table. For each one correct they get a point!

Mighty PE tips

◆ Call out a question. Whatever the answer is, the children must run around the room in character, eg jumping, cycling etc.

◆ Put characters in each corner of the hall or field. Shout out a question and the class must run to that character, eg if you shout 2 x 5, they must run to 400m Sinitta and shout 10.

◆ Get the children to chant their times tables as they are doing star jumps, sit ups etc – don't stop until they reach a given number.

◆ Do laps of the playground in character eg jumping, running, pretending to swim. How far into the tables can they get each lap?

◆ Use a parachute. Give every child a multiple. Call out a question. If they are the answer they must run under to get to the other side before they are caught underneath. The other children must count to the answer before they can try to trap them; for example, if the question was 4 x 5, they must count to 20 before putting the parachute down.

◆ Count in 5s, 10s, etc as you throw a ball to a partner.

◆ Put numbers around the room – run around the room and collect as many multiples of 2, 4 etc as you can. You can change this by shouting out different movements such as hop, skip etc.

- Hopscotch – counting in 2, 3, 4, etc – use chalk to mark on the playground.

- Tennis – as you hit the ball, count in your table. If you miss the ball you must count back in your table before you can start again – how far can you get?

- Use the tables when you are giving out equipment, eg there are 20 balls, 5 groups, how many balls can each group have?

Mighty cross-curricular tips

There is no reason why the Mighty Multiples can't integrate into many different areas of the curriculum. Bringing them into different areas helps the children to become familiar with the characters and, even more importantly, allows them to learn how to use times tables in everyday real life situations. Below are a few examples:

- **Design and technology**
  When chopping fruit, sort the slices into groups of 2s or 4s. Talk about groups. Work out how many you have altogether by multiplying the number in the group by the amount of groups. This helps children to visualize groups.

  When making vehicles, talk to the class. Ask them how many wheels you will need to order if each car has 4 wheels and you have 20 children in the class, etc.

- **History**
  If there were 20 children coming to a VE day party and they were rationed to 40 cakes, how many cakes could they each have?

- **Science**
  Multiply all the parts of the body that we have 2 of, eg eyes, by 7. What's the answer?

- **Geography**
  On your journey to school you see 8 post boxes. How many post boxes do you see in a week?

- **Music**
  Sing the Mighty Multiple songs!

Activities included in the Mighty Multiples scheme

Using the character masks

◆ Choose a number of children to stand at the front wearing a mask. Give all of the other children a number that is a multiple of one of the character's times table. Each child has to give their multiple to the correct character.

◆ Choose as many characters as you like and get children to wear the masks. Hide numbers around the room. Put a timer on and see how many multiples they can collect.

◆ Place a mystery character mask on someone's head. Get the other children to give multiples of that character's number. See how many numbers it takes to guess.

◆ In your PE lessons, stick the masks on the wall. Shout a number and the pupils have to run to a character that the number could be a factor of.

◆ Get everyone to wear a mask. Pair up with someone wearing the same mask. In pairs the children throw the ball to each other counting in their number. Or to step up the game, you could mix characters and say your next number as you catch, instead of taking turns!

◆ Have a big box of balls. Give the child a character and they have to divide the balls by that number.

◆ Throw a die and multiply your character's number by the number thrown!

Using the number fans

◆ Give out a range of Mighty Multiple number fans. Pick one person to be 'coach'. The coach says any times table question and whoever has the answer on their fan stands up.

◆ Choose one person to be a Mighty Multiple character. See how fast children can find a multiple of the character's table.

◆ Give all children the same number fan. Ask them all to stand up. Call out a times table question. The slowest to find the answer sits down. Repeat until one winner is left standing. You can alter this game by having everyone jogging on the spot or balancing on one leg, etc, or by asking division questions.

◆ One child is a character at the front,

eg Long Jump Jim. The rest of the class has the corresponding number fan. The character calls out a question, eg 1 x 10, and the other children show him the answer as quickly as they can.

◆ Get everyone into character, eg Long Jump Jim. Everyone has to jump as they find the answer to your question on their fan. This way they are not only thinking of the answer, but also which times tables they had to use to get the answer.

Using the visual grouping sheets

It is very important that children understand the meaning of the 'x' symbol in any given number sentence. From the early stages children can count out groups of objects and place them into the visual grouping shapes on the sheet (eg shoes for 2 times table) to visualize their multiplication sentence.

As they progress and gain confidence in doing this, they can move on to drawing out the groups independently. These sheets can be used further into the scheme to visually show dividing.

On each visual grouping sheet an example is given, showing how to use it if multiplying by 2. If you don't wish the children to see this, cover up the example before photocopying.

◆ Give every child in the class a multiplication or division sentence (you can tailor the complexity to the individual child according to ability). Get each child to use their visual grouping sheet to answer the question as quickly as they can. They can stand up when they have completed the sheet to earn a reward!

◆ Laminate visual grouping sheets and use them during whole class teaching, so that every child can participate and you will be able to quickly see who has grasped the concept well.

◆ Get children to work in pairs, writing questions for each other to complete on their visual grouping sheets. They can then mark them, awarding a point for each correct answer. Children keep a tally to find the winner.

◆ In the middle of each table in your room have a pile of questions on flash cards. Set a time limit and allow children to select a card at a time to answer on their visual grouping sheet. Who can compete the most in the time limit? Can they beat their personal best next time?

Using the badges

The Mighty Multiple badges can be used in a variety of ways. They can be used as rewards or as teaching aids.

◆ Use the badges to teach factors. Give every child a different badge. Say a number and ask all the children who have matching badges to stand up. For example, if you said the number 24, the children who were holding Backstroke Brenda, Freestyle Freda, 400 metre

Sinitta and Triple Jump Tracey would stand up. You can extend this by giving half the class numbers and half the class badges. Then let them find an appropriate partner. They may have to swap around to find the perfect solution!

◆ Have a basket of badges. Call a child to the front to pick out a badge. The child then has to name the character on the badge and think of a number sentence the character would be likely to ask. For example if I pulled out Shot Put Tony, I may say, '2 x 9 = 18' or I may say '2 x 9 =' and ask my classmates to answer the question.

◆ Pick two or four different times tables that you wish to practise, and divide your class into groups, according to which of the chosen tables you would like them to focus on. Choose a wall to represent each table and put all of the multiples of that times table onto that wall. Call out a question. The team that corresponds to the question has to run and collect the appropriate answer to earn a badge. You may wish to count the badges at the end to find a winning team.

◆ A child selects a badge out of the basket and says what times table it is. Then he/she rolls a die and multiplies the number rolled by their times table. Repeat. How many can they do in 20 seconds?

Using the songs and poems

Research has shown that from an early age many children find it easier to learn facts through songs and poetry. For this reason we decided that we would accompany each times table with an appropriate song and poem to learn! Many of the songs follow familiar age-appropriate tunes and should be great fun for all ages!

All the poems and songs are recorded on CD1. In addition there are instrumental versions on CD2, enabling pupils to perform 'karaoke' style, or to add additional verses. (See page 181 for a list of the CDs contents.)

Songs may be learnt both as a class and as a whole school. You can use them to introduce a new times table and they are a great way to introduce the characters. They can also be used as a consolidation technique. Songs can be learnt in school or at home. They can be used in singing assemblies, music sessions or as background music in the classroom.

Why not use the poems as part of a poetry competition? Dress up as the character and have a poetry recital. This of course allows cross-curricular learning!

The songs need not just be used in music lessons. How about using them in PE sessions? You could choreograph a simple dance routine

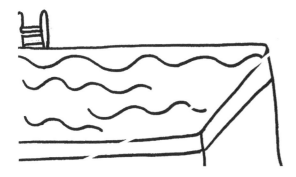

to go with each song or use them as part of a game. For example you could rap Shot Put Tony's rap while throwing a ball to each other counting in 9s.

Use the songs as a whole school exercise session in the morning, waking up the mind and body before a day at school. Ask some children to put together a routine to one of the songs. Get the children and staff to sing and dance along for 5 minutes every day.

Why not invite parents to come and join in once a term? They can contribute for the pleasure of doing so, allowing you to use this as a fund-raising opportunity and also to share learning.

Using the 144 grid

◆ Colour in all the multiples of any given number.

◆ Give everyone a copy of the grid. Shout out a question and the children have to use the grid to find out the answer. The first to find it has to stand up and jog on the spot until everyone is up and jogging!

◆ Call out a question and the children have to colour the answer on their grid. See

how many they can get correct!

◆ Throw a counter onto the grid. Whatever number it lands on, they must shout out the question, eg if it lands on 81 they must shout out, '9 x 9 is 81.'

◆ Get into pairs. Each has a different times table. Take 5-10 minutes to see who can colour more multiples of their number. Or use the same grid as your partner and race to see how many you can get. If your partner's multiples overlap, it's a race to see who can secure/colour that number first.

◆ Have some missing numbers on the grid. Give the children 10 minutes to fill in the gaps. This can of course be tailored according to ability.

Using the bingo game boards

The bingo boards are a valuable resource in the classroom. They can be used for independent and adult-led learning.

◆ Play bingo in the traditional way! Give every child a board, tell them the multiplication table(s) you will be focusing on. They must first fill in their blank bingo board with possible answers. Then you, as the teacher (or a chosen child), reads out the multiplication question. If they have the answer on their board, they can cross it off. The winner is the first to mark off all their answers and shout out 'Mighty Multiples'. Once there is a claimed winner, they must justify their win, by calling out the given questions again and matching them to their answers. For a simpler version of this basic game, teachers could pre-fill the bingo boards with answers.

◆ Draw out giant bingo boards on the floor and fill in the answers. Get children to

look at the numbers. They have to think of a question to match the answer on the board. If they get it right they can stand on the answer. Can you manage to fill the whole board?

◆ Make four giant versions of the boards. Fill the boxes with questions rather than answers. Put them in four different places around the classroom/hall/playground. Put the answers on cards in the middle of the space. Divide the class up into four teams and assign them each a bingo board. Once the whistle blows, one member of each team has to run into the centre and collect an answer to match a question on their board and return to the board to place the answer on top of the appropriate question. Once the team has verified the answer as correct, the next member can run to get an answer. There should only ever be four children running at once. The winning team will fill their board first!

Starting a Mighty Multiples' Club in your school

Why have a club?

Starting a Mighty Multiples' club in your school provides further encouragement for children to enjoy learning their times table in a fun, interactive manner. It will also help them to become independent and self-motivated learners.

Schools have found that it works well to have a small Mighty Multiples' club of children of mixed ability, who are keen and enthusiastic and enjoy taking part. The club should not be seen as something children are forced to go to or as an 'extra homework' type club.

We have found that it works well when older children, who have perhaps completed the challenge or are close to doing so, actually run the club. They enjoy thinking of their own games and challenges to make learning the tables fun and active. In doing so you extend peer learning and stretch your more able mathematicians.

When shall we run a club?

This is entirely up to you and when it suits your school. It could be after school or even during lunchtime!

How long should the club be?

Again this is up to you, however, we wouldn't recommend the club to be longer than 30–45 minutes! Remember, it's quality not quantity!

How shall we group our club?

You have two options:
◆　Either keep everyone in one group – if it's a whole school challenge then why not work together?
◆　Or split the club into a KS1 and KS2 club.

Both ways have been highly successful and thoroughly enjoyed!

Don't forget to pick out lots of ideas on pages 11–14 to help you make sessions extra fun. Equally important, allow your clubs members to add their own unique touches to the club, making it even more exciting.

Mighty Multiples' in-built assessment

Mighty Multiples is designed to be motivating and rewarding. With this is mind, assessment challenges were designed to adopt these philosophies, whilst also ultimately gathering the assessment material on each pupil's knowledge for you, the teacher.

Below is an outline of how, when and why to use each type of reward and assessment included in the challenge.

1. The 2-minute weekly challenge (page 22)

This can be used each week as a quick, fun and stress free assessment tool. Simply place a times table suitable for each child in the middle and give them 2 minutes to multiply that number by all the numbers around the edge of the track. You, of course, can use this at any point in your week where you have a few minutes to spare. This informal assessment can also be used as a practice tool.

2. The speedy challenge (page 23)

This can be used as a revision tool or as an informal assessment if you are unsure if a child is ready for the formal assessments.

3. The formal assessments

You will find the formal assessments at the end of each number bond or times table unit. These are to be used when you feel that a child is secure in their knowledge of a table and ready to be assessed to move on. It is up to individual teachers or schools to decide how long to allow for these assessments. We suggest 5–10 minutes per assessment. If it is taking a lot longer than this without a reason, the child probably isn't secure enough in their knowledge yet. It is important that children complete the number and word problem challenges at the same time; ie if they are sitting the 2 times table challenge (page 61), they should also to do the 2 times table word problem challenge (page 62) as well.

4. Certificates

As well as the obvious bronze, silver, gold and platinum certificates, please remember to continue to motivate and acknowledge those that put in the effort but perhaps find the challenge harder. This is the purpose of the 'good progress certificate' (page 24) and the 'congratulations, you have completed an assessment certificates' (page 25). All the certifcates may also be downloaded from our website: www.brilliantpublications.co.uk/book/the-mighty-multiples-times-table-challenge-381.

5. Picture chart (page 26)

Provide your pupils with a visual record of what they have achieved, and what they are working towards. Allow them to fill this in as they go along!

6. The teacher record sheet (page 27)

This is for you to assess and track your pupils' progress.

Mighty Multiples'
2-minute weekly challenge

Write your times table in the star in the middle and times each number around the track by it.
Write the answers on the track.

Mighty Multiples'
Speedy challenge

Write your table in the first column then write as many different number sentences as you can in the remaining boxes.

Table				
1 x =				
2 x =				

Can you write some word problems to go with your questions?

Mighty Multiples
Good Progress
Certificate

Congratulations!

Awarded to

_____

On

_____

You are making great progress
working towards:

_____

_____

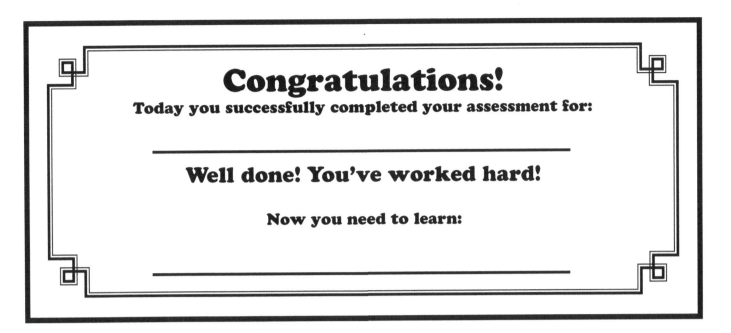

Congratulations!

Today you successfully completed your assessment for:

_____

Well done! You've worked hard!

Now you need to learn:

_____

Congratulations!

Today you successfully completed your assessment for:

_____

Well done! You've worked hard!

Now you need to learn:

_____

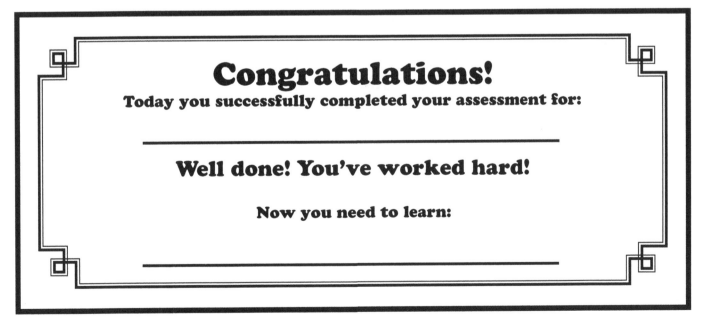

Congratulations!

Today you successfully completed your assessment for:

_____

Well done! You've worked hard!

Now you need to learn:

_____

Mighty Multiples'
Times table challenge

Name _____

Class _____

When your teacher informs you that you have successfully completed each table, colour in the character below:

Bronze Award
100m Peter (number stories)
200m Travis (number bonds)

Silver Award
400m Sinitta (2x table)
Long Jump Jim (10 x table)
Javelin John (5x table)
Freestyle Freda (4x table)

Gold Award
High Jump Heather (3x table)
Backstroke Brenda (6x table)
Cycling Susie (7x table)
Triple Jump Tracey (8x table)
Shot Put Tony (9x table)
High Dive Clive (mixed, 1)
Triathlon Saffron (mixed, 2)

Platinum Award
1000m Glenda (11x table)
Aerobic Alan (12x table)

Mighty Multiples' Teacher record sheet

Class _____

Name	Bronze		Silver				Gold								Platinum	
	Stories	Bonds	2x	10x	5x	4x	3x	6x	7x	8x	9x	Mixed 1	Mixed 2	11x	12x
	A | B	A | B	A | B	A | B	A | B	A | B	A | B	A | B	A | B	A | B	A | B	A | B	A | B	A | B	A | B

A = Times table challenge
B = Word problem challenge

Dear Parents and Guardians,

Having reviewed our school mathematics teaching, it has become apparent that areas for development are times tables, word problems and division. Therefore, we are introducing a new scheme called **The Mighty Multiples Times Table Challenge**. It includes a number of sporting characters which will help your child to learn their number bonds and multiplications. Children progress around an athletic racecourse towards the ultimate goal of a Platinum Award, awarded for secure knowledge of all areas.

It is not simply a case of being able to chant the tables, but also being able to use them within mathematics to, for example, solve word problems and divide. For this reason, to be able to achieve each award, your child will have to not only recite the tables, but also be able to complete challenges, which cover word problems and division.

The scheme is made up of four awards:

Bronze award
Before your child moves into the first times table challenge, they will need to complete a number story and number bond challenge.

Silver award
To achieve the Silver Award they must complete the 2, 5, 10 and 4 times table challenges.

Gold award
The Gold Award includes the 3, 6, 7, 8, 9, and mixed table challenges.

Platinum award
The Platinum Award is awarded for completing all levels, including the 11 and 12 times tables challenges.

Each class will have **The Mighty Multiples Times Table Challenge** explained to them by their teacher. All formal assessments, to move onto the next challenge, will take place in class. There will also be a whole class chart in each classroom, to mark each child's success.

We very much look forward to working with you to make this a fun and successful challenge. If you have any further questions please contact your class teachers.

Many thanks

The maths team

Mighty Multiples'
Top times table tips

Make learning times tables fun!

Remember there are rules that can help you!

Any number multiplied by 0 is always 0!

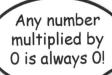

To multiply by 4, times by 2 and double it!

Silly rhymes and songs can help too! Try these ones or why not make up your own!

Aerobic Alan twirled and twirled then fell to the floor – 12 12s are 144.

High Jump Heather scores three and three in a line, 3 x 3 is number 9.

8 x 8 fell on the floor. Tracey picked it up, it was 64!

Be practical! Be active!

When you go up to bed, take the stairs in 2s!

Sing the times table in the voice you imagine your character would use, or mime their actions for each table!

Use chalk to draw stepping stones and hopscotch grids with your challenge in, eg 5, 10, 15, 20 …

Mighty Multiples' tips for Learning times tables on the way to school!

Ask your child questions such as:

• If we pass 3 post boxes on the way to school each day and 3 on the way home, how many post boxes do we see in a week?

• If the post man has to deliver 6 letters to every road we walk/drive down on our route to school, how many letters will he have to deliver altogether?

Speed test
See how many times table questions your child can answer, by that lamp post, before the end of the road etc. Mix them up a bit. Don't always do them in order!

Look at and recognize house numbers. Follow one side of the road and note they count in 2s. Count along with them!

See if you can match a question to each house number. For example, this house is number 20: what times 2 makes 20?

Play times table 'ping pong'. You start with a number. Your child gives the next number and you continue until you get stuck! Use any times table, eg 3, 6, 9, 12, etc. Start this on Monday and use the same table all week. How high can you get by Friday?

Give your child something to spot – for example red cars, for each red car they see they can count with their table number – give another child a different thing to spot and they can race – who can spot more and therefore gain the most points?!

Mighty Multiples' tips for
Learning times tables at the supermarket!

Give your children challenges to work out that will involve their tables. For example, there are 6 people in our family and to make this recipe we need to buy 2 carrots per person. How many do we need?

Ask your child to get you 12 apples, etc. Ask them to count them in 3s as they pick them. How many lots of 3 did they have to get before they had 12?

If every person in our family eats 2 apples a day, how many do we need to buy for the week?

Find a box of chocolates. Explain that the box has 20 chocolates in it. How many can everyone in the family have if we divide them equally?

Give your child a list of items to get. Ask them to count in 2s (for example) until they have all those items. How far did they get?

Use your tables to count how many baskets there are in a pile, or how many trolleys there are in a row!

Give your child a list of items to get – for each one they put in the basket they can have 2 points (could be any amount of points according to their table) They must use their times table to count how many points they have!

Ask your child word problems. For example, if we have 5 oranges, 5 lemons, 5 apples and 5 bananas, how many pieces of fruit do we have altogether?

Count in your tables to see how far you can get before all your shopping is packed into the car!

Mighty Multiples' tips for Learning times tables at the park!

Whilst on the swing, recite your tables, only counting on as you go forwards and back! How far can you get before you get stuck? Race with a friend on another swing. The faster you go, the quicker you'll get higher!

Choose a friend to go on the seesaw with. As you go up, say a number question and see if your friend can answer it before you get to the top. For example, if you say 1 x 10, your friend will have to answer 10. When your friend goes up they ask you a question! Who can get the most correct?

If there are 2 swings and 8 children, how many times will the swings need to be used before everyone can have a go? Asking everyday questions like this will allow you to bring tables into real life situations!

Time how long your friend can run round the playground, counting in 2s, 3s, etc.

Speed counting. How far can you get up your tables before you reach the end of the slide? You can take it in turns. Try to beat your friends!

Throw a ball to your partner and count in your chosen times table. Either both count on from each other or have a different times table each. If you drop the ball count back to zero.

Play football with a twist! Decide on a times table, eg 6 times table. For each goal you get 6 points. Imagine how impressed your family will be when you tell them you won your match 60-36!

100m Peter's Number stories activities

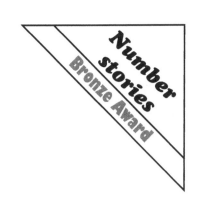

Story of 1	Story of 2	Story of 3	Story of 4	Story of 5
0 + 1 = 1 1 + 0 = 1	0 + 2 = 2 2 + 0 = 2 1 + 1 = 2	0 + 3 = 3 1 + 2 = 3 2 + 1 = 3 3 + 0 = 3	0 + 4 = 4 1 + 3 = 4 2 + 2 = 4 3 + 1 = 4 4 + 0 = 4	0 + 5 = 5 1 + 4 = 5 2 + 3 = 5 3 + 2 = 5 4 + 1 = 5 5 + 0 = 5
Story of 6	**Story of 7**	**Story of 8**	**Story of 9**	**Story of 10**
0 + 6 = 6 1 + 5 = 6 2 + 4 = 6 3 + 3 = 6 4 + 2 = 6 5 + 1 = 6 6 + 0 = 6	0 + 7 = 7 1 + 6 = 7 2 + 5 = 7 3 + 4 = 7 4 + 3 = 7 5 + 2 = 7 6 + 1 = 7 7 + 0 = 7	0 + 8 = 8 1 + 7 = 8 2 + 6 = 8 3 + 5 = 8 4 + 4 = 8 5 + 3 = 8 6 + 2 = 8 7 + 1 = 8 8 + 0 = 8	0 + 9 = 9 1 + 8 = 9 2 + 7 = 9 3 + 6 = 9 4 + 5 = 9 5 + 4 = 9 6 + 3 = 9 7 + 2 = 9 8 + 1 = 9 9 + 0 = 9	0 + 10 = 10 1 + 9 = 10 2 + 8 = 10 3 + 7 = 10 4 + 6 = 10 5 + 5 = 10 6 + 4 = 10 7 + 3 = 10 8 + 2 = 10 9 + 1 = 10 10 + 0 = 10

100m Peter's
Number stories

Story of 1	Story of 2	Story of 3	Story of 4	Story of 5
0 + 1 = 1 1 + 0 = 1	0 + 2 = 2 2 + 0 = 2 1 + 1 = 2	0 + 3 = 3 1 + 2 = 3 2 + 1 = 3 3 + 0 = 3	0 + 4 = 4 1 + 3 = 4 2 + 2 = 4 3 + 1 = 4 4 + 0 = 4	0 + 5 = 5 1 + 4 = 5 2 + 3 = 5 3 + 2 = 5 4 + 1 = 5 5 + 0 = 5
Story of 6	Story of 7	Story of 8	Story of 9	Story of 10
0 + 6 = 6 1 + 5 = 6 2 + 4 = 6 3 + 3 = 6 4 + 2 = 6 5 + 1 = 6 6 + 0 = 6	0 + 7 = 7 1 + 6 = 7 2 + 5 = 7 3 + 4 = 7 4 + 3 = 7 5 + 2 = 7 6 + 1 = 7 7 + 0 = 7	0 + 8 = 8 1 + 7 = 8 2 + 6 = 8 3 + 5 = 8 4 + 4 = 8 5 + 3 = 8 6 + 2 = 8 7 + 1 = 8 8 + 0 = 8	0 + 9 = 9 1 + 8 = 9 2 + 7 = 9 3 + 6 = 9 4 + 5 = 9 5 + 4 = 9 6 + 3 = 9 7 + 2 = 9 8 + 1 = 9 9 + 0 = 9	0 + 10 = 10 1 + 9 = 10 2 + 8 = 10 3 + 7 = 10 4 + 6 = 10 5 + 5 = 10 6 + 4 = 10 7 + 3 = 10 8 + 2 = 10 9 + 1 = 10 10 + 0 = 10

100m Peter's
Number fans

1

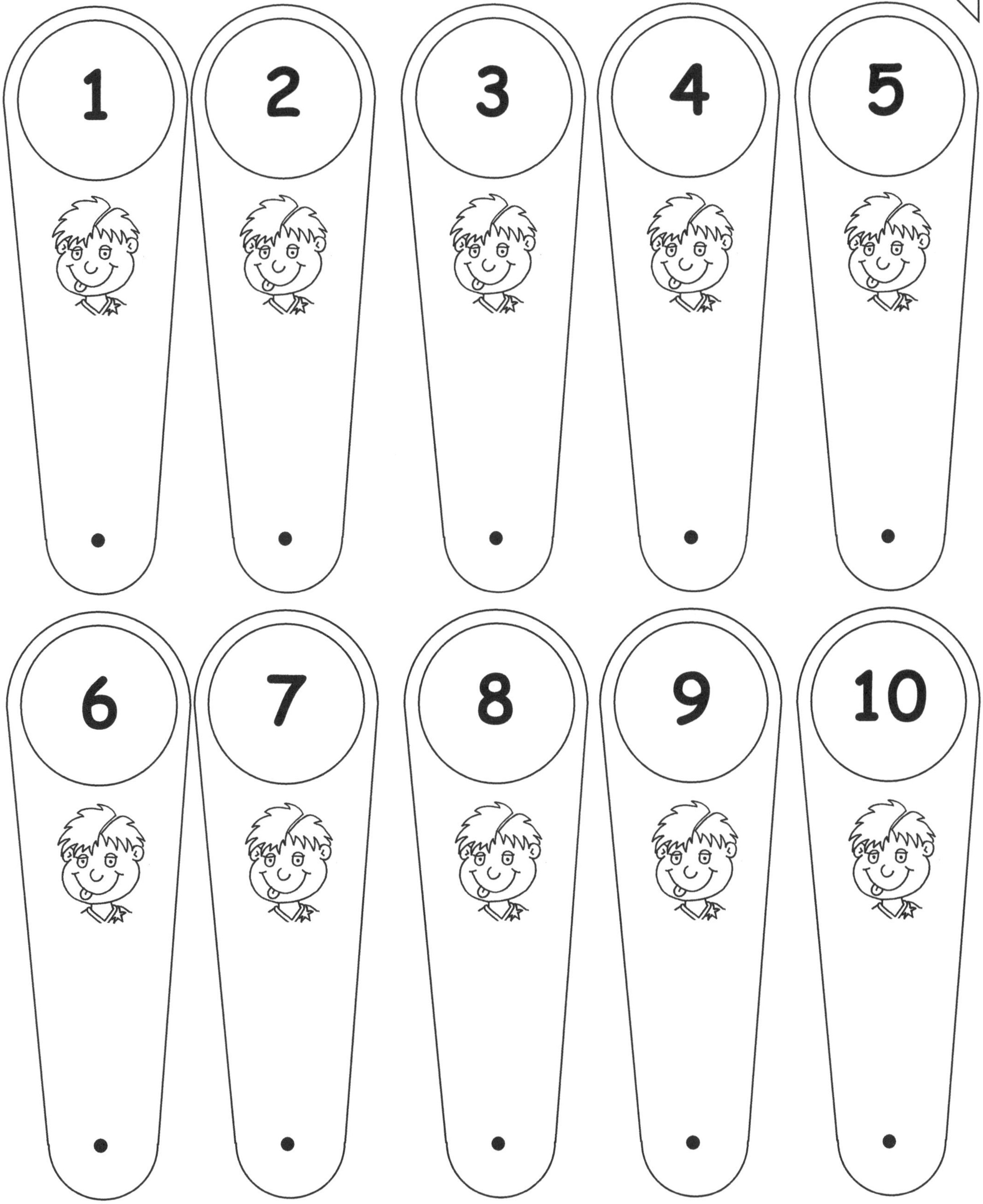

2

3

4

5

6

7

8

9

10

The Mighty Multiples Times Table Challenge
35

100m Peter's Badges

100m Peter's
Character mask

Colour in your character mask. Then cut out and stick to a band of card, ready to place around your head.

The Mighty Multiples Times Table Challenge

100m Peter's
Number stories poem

Track
●
2

100m Peter is speeding around the track
We want to add to 10 to get a pat on the back!

The track goes round and round
As we twist our sums around.
Let's start with 0
And see what we can find.

0 plus 10?
Peter's overtaken Ben!
10 and 0?
Peter is such a hero.

1 add 9?
Peter runs towards the line.
9 plus 1?
Peter's really having fun.

2 add 8?
Peter's looking really great.
8 add 2?
Peter passes Gemma too.

3 add 7?
Peter's in number bond heaven.
7 plus 3?
Peter is so fast, you see.

4 plus 6?
Peter shows his adding tricks.
6 plus 4?
Peter overtakes two more.

5 add 5?
Peter dives across the line.
There's no more twisting in this game
5 add 5 always stays the same.

Now Peter's crossed the line,
He is feeling mighty fine!
Give yourselves a pat on the back
You've run right round the Number Bond Track!

100m Peter's
Number stories song

Tracks
●
15 & 28

Number
stories
Bronze Award

(Children run on the spot when singing and do the actions! They can also change the actions!)

1 + 9 is 10
9 + 1 is 10
Peter runs
Peter runs
1 + 9 is 10

2 + 8 is 10
8 + 2 is 10
Peter jumps
Peter jumps
2 + 8 is 10

3 + 7 is 10
7 + 3 is 10
Peter sprints
Peter sprints
3 + 7 is 10

4 + 6 is 10
6 + 4 is 10
Peter waves
Peter waves
4 + 6 is 10

5 + 5 is 10
5 + 5 is 10
Peter wins
Peter wins
5 + 5 is 10

Hooray!

Sung to the tune of 'The Grand Old Duke of York'.

100m Peter's Number stories challenge

$$1 + \bigcirc = 10$$

$$5 + \bigcirc = 10$$

$$6 + \bigcirc = 10$$

$$\bigcirc + 3 = 10$$

$$\bigcirc + 8 = 10$$

$$\bigcirc + 7 = 10$$

$$\bigcirc + 4 = 10$$

$$10 + \bigcirc = 10$$

$$4 + \bigcirc = 10$$

$$\bigcirc + 10 = 10$$

$$3 + \bigcirc = 10$$

$$7 + \bigcirc = 10$$

$$9 + \bigcirc = 10$$

$$\bigcirc + 5 = 10$$

$$\bigcirc + 9 = 10$$

$$\bigcirc + 6 = 10$$

$$2 + \bigcirc = 10$$

$$\bigcirc + 2 = 10$$

$$\bigcirc + 1 = 10$$

$$8 + \bigcirc = 10$$

100m Peter's Number stories word problem challenge

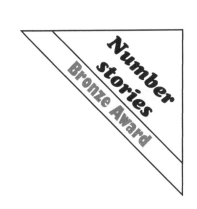

1. Peter has 9 sweets but there are 10 people in his race. He wants to give everyone one sweet. How many more sweets does he need?

2. Peter has 10 medals, 5 are silver and the rest are gold. How many gold ones are there?

3. There are 8 runners at the starting line but there need to be 10. How many runners are missing?

4. Peter needs to run 10 laps of the track. He has already run 3 laps. How many more does he have to go?

5. Altogether Peter has 10 running vests. At the moment 6 are in the wash. How many are not in the wash?

200m Travis's Number bonds activities

Number bonds to 10

0	+	10	=	10
1	+	9	=	10
2	+	8	=	10
3	+	7	=	10
4	+	6	=	10
5	+	5	=	10
6	+	4	=	10
7	+	3	=	10
8	+	2	=	10
9	+	1	=	10
10	+	0	=	10

Number bonds to 20

0	+	20	=	20
1	+	19	=	20
2	+	18	=	20
3	+	17	=	20
4	+	16	=	20
5	+	15	=	20
6	+	14	=	20
7	+	13	=	20
8	+	12	=	20
9	+	11	=	20
10	+	10	=	20
11	+	9	=	10
12	+	8	=	20
13	+	7	=	20
14	+	6	=	20
15	+	5	=	20
16	+	4	=	20
17	+	3	=	20
18	+	2	=	20
19	+	1	=	20
20	+	0	=	20

Skip
15 + 5 =

Jump backwards
12 + 8 =

Wave
1 + 19 =

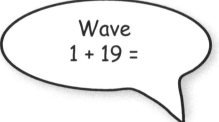

They should add up to 20 or 10.

200m Travis's
Number bonds

Number bonds to 10

0	+ 10	=	10
1	+ 9	=	10
2	+ 8	=	10
3	+ 7	=	10
4	+ 6	=	10
5	+ 5	=	10
6	+ 4	=	10
7	+ 3	=	10
8	+ 2	=	10
9	+ 1	=	10
10	+ 0	=	10

Number bonds to 20

0	+ 20	=	20
1	+ 19	=	20
2	+ 18	=	20
3	+ 17	=	20
4	+ 16	=	20
5	+ 15	=	20
6	+ 14	=	20
7	+ 13	=	20
8	+ 12	=	20
9	+ 11	=	20
10	+ 10	=	20
11	+ 9	=	10
12	+ 8	=	20
13	+ 7	=	20
14	+ 6	=	20
15	+ 5	=	20
16	+ 4	=	20
17	+ 3	=	20
18	+ 2	=	20
19	+ 1	=	20
20	+ 0	=	20

200m Travis's Number fans, 1

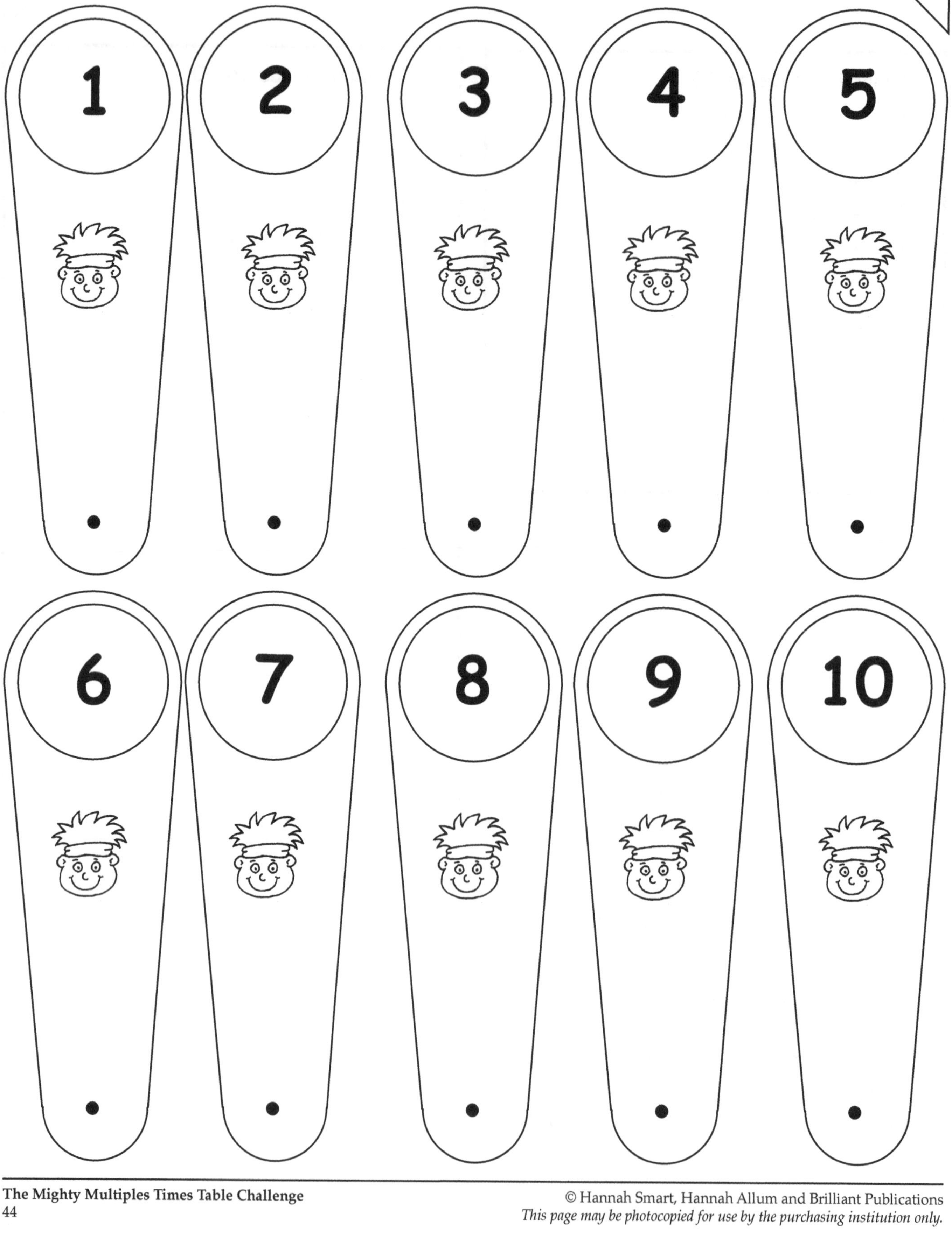

1

2

3

4

5

6

7

8

9

10

200m Travis's
Number fans, 2

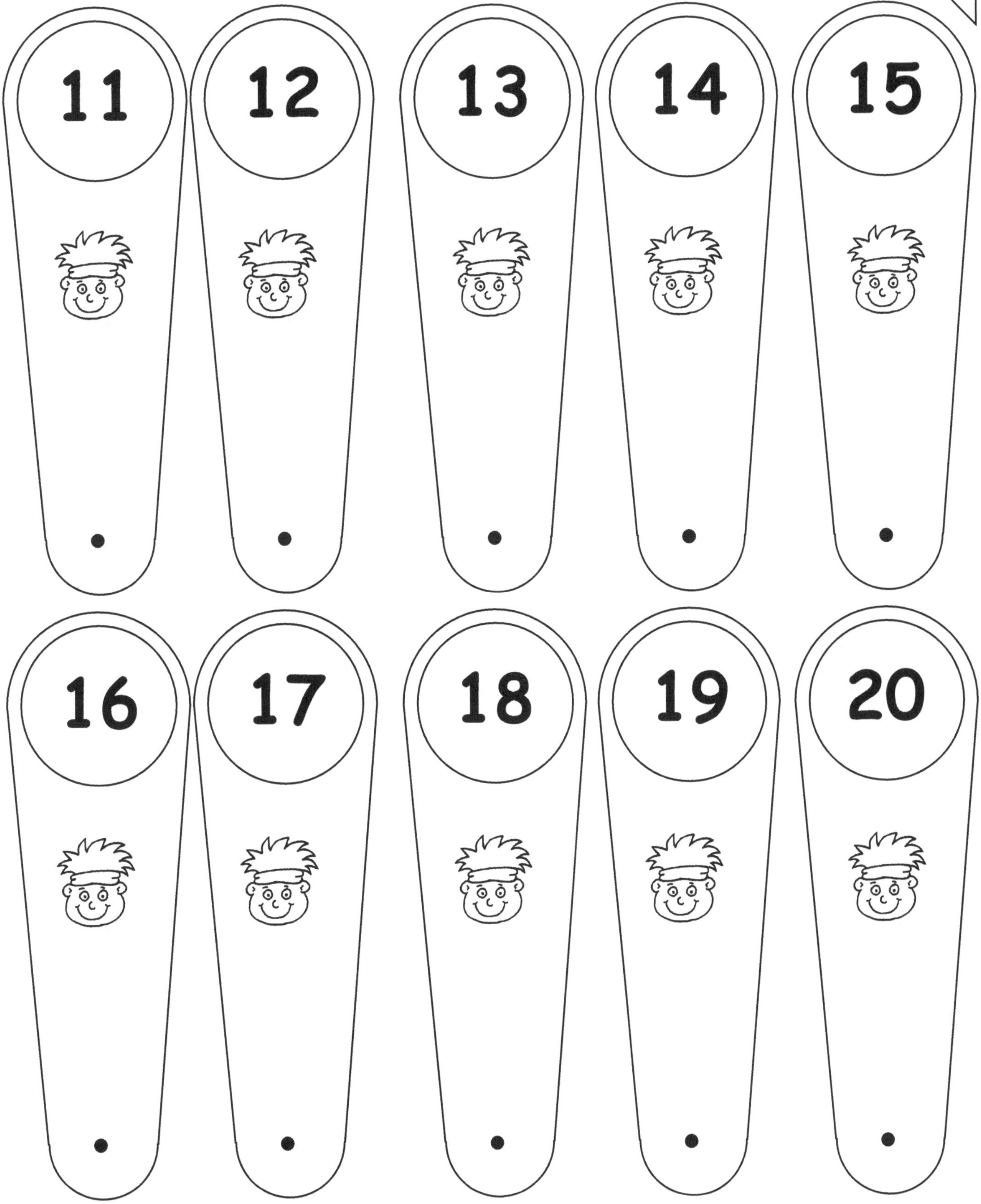

11

12

13

14

15

16

17

18

19

20

The Mighty Multiples Times Table Challenge

200m Travis's
Badges

200m Travis's
Character mask

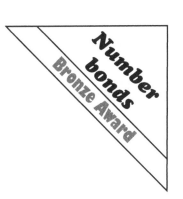

Colour in your character
mask. Then cut out and stick
to a band of card, ready to
place around your head.

The Mighty Multiples Times Table Challenge

200m Travis's
Number bonds poem

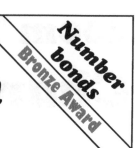

Track
3

200m Travis runs around the track
Adding to 20, he really has the knack.

1 plus 19? Is the same as 19 add 1
Making 20, Travis knows how that's done!

2 add 18? That's the same as 18 add 2
Wow! Watch Travis – that lap he really flew!

17 plus 3? Is the same as 3 add 17
When it comes to running Travis is keen!

4 plus 16? That's the same as 16 plus 4
Racing makes Travis want to run even more!

5 add 15? That's the same as 15 add 5
Travis waves to the crowd and gives a high 5.

6 add 14? Well that equals 14 plus 6
Wow look at you, you're no longer in a mix.

7 plus 13? That's the same as 13 add 7
Quick speed up Travis, you can overtake Kevin!

8 add 12? That equals 12 plus 8
When it comes to running, Travis is really great!

9 add 11? That's equal to 11 plus 9
You can hear Travis shout, 'that medal will be mine!'

10 plus 10? No it can't be changed
Neither can the winner, it's Travis again!

If like Travis you know this rhyme
A shiny bronze medal will be yours in no time!

200m Travis's
Number bonds song

Tracks
16 & 29

Chorus
Travis runs around the track, round the track, round the track,
Travis runs around the track as he counts to 20!

1 + 19 is 20 he says, 20 he says, 20 he says
19 + 1 is 20 he says, it's easy to count to 20.
Chorus

2 + 18 is 20 he says, 20 he says, 20 he says
18 + 2 is 20 he says, it's easy to count to 20.
Chorus

3 + 17 is 20 he says, 20 he says, 20 he says
17 + 3 is 20 he says, it's easy to count to 20.
Chorus

4 + 16 is 20 he says, 20 he says, 20 he says
16 + 4 is 20 he says, it's easy to count to 20.
Chorus

5 + 15 is 20 he says, 20 he says, 20 he says
15 + 5 is 20 he says, it's easy to count to 20.
Chorus

6 + 14 is 20 he says, 20 he says, 20 he says
14 + 6 is 20 he says, it's easy to count to 20.
Chorus

7 + 13 is 20 he says, 20 he says, 20 he says
13 + 7 is 20 he says, it's easy to count to 20.
Chorus

8 + 12 is 20 he says, 20 he says, 20 he says
12 + 8 is 20 he says, it's easy to count to 20.
Chorus

9 + 11 is 20 he says, 20 he says, 20 he says
11 + 9 is 20 he says, it's easy to count to 20.
Chorus

10 + 10 is 20 he says, 20 he says, 20 he says
10 + 10 is 20 he says, now we can count to 20!
Chorus

Sung to the tune of 'Mary had a Little Lamb'.

The Mighty Multiples Times Table Challenge

200m Travis's Number bonds challenge

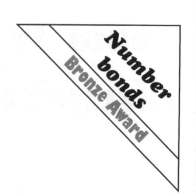

There are 21 ways to make 20 by adding two numbers together.
See how many you can remember. Write each way in a different box.

Start	

200m Travis's Number bonds word problem challenge

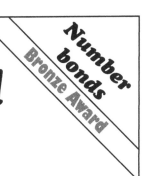

1. Travis has 16 energy drinks. He needs 1 bottle for each of the 20 athletes in the race. How many more does he need?

2. 12 people out of 20 have crossed the finish line. How many are still running?

3. In total, 200m Travis ran 2 laps in 20 seconds. The first lap took him 11 seconds. How long did the second lap take him?

4. Travis has a target of winning 20 medals. So far he has won 6. How many more does he need until he reaches his target?

5. To watch his Olympic performance Travis was given 20 tickets. So far he has invited 4 people. How many more can he invite?

Mighty Multiples

Bronze Award

Congratulations!

Awarded to

_____

On

_____

You have successfully completed the following awards:

100m
Peter

200m
Travis

400m Sinitta's
2 times table activities

1	×	**2**	=	2
2	×	**2**	=	4
3	×	**2**	=	6
4	×	**2**	=	8
5	×	**2**	=	10
6	×	**2**	=	12
7	×	**2**	=	14
8	×	**2**	=	16
9	×	**2**	=	18
10	×	**2**	=	20
11	×	**2**	=	22
12	×	**2**	=	24

Shout your times tables to be heard above the crowds!

On your way to bed jump up the stairs in 2s.

Try to run as fast as me, while singing your times tables.

Time yourself to run to the door then times your score by 2! Who is faster, you or your Mum?

400m Sinitta's
2 times table

1	×	**2**	=	2
2	×	**2**	=	4
3	×	**2**	=	6
4	×	**2**	=	8
5	×	**2**	=	10
6	×	**2**	=	12
7	×	**2**	=	14
8	×	**2**	=	16
9	×	**2**	=	18
10	×	**2**	=	20
11	×	**2**	=	22
12	×	**2**	=	24

400m Sinitta's Number fans

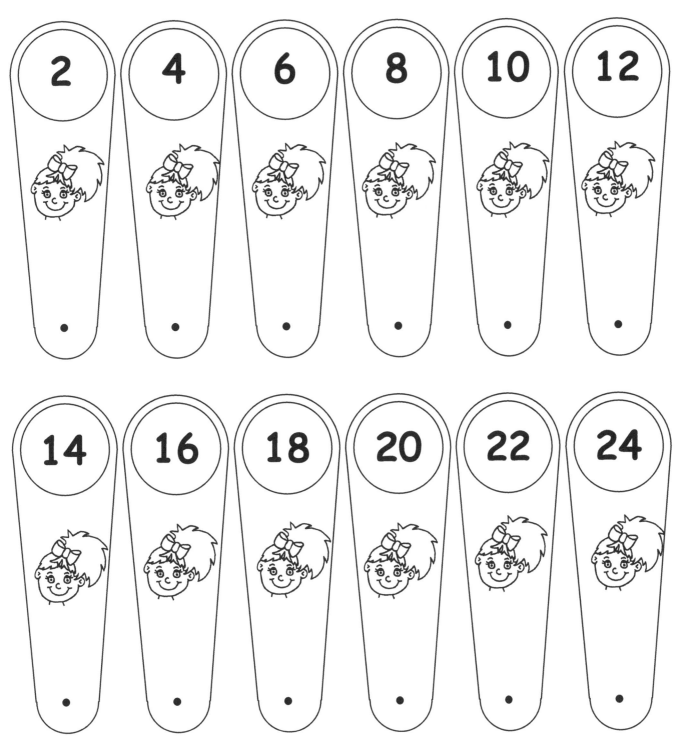

400m Sinitta's
Visual grouping

2 x ___ = ____

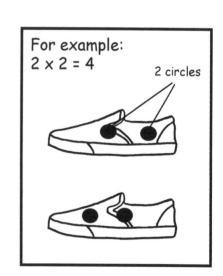

For example:
2 x 2 = 4

2 circles

400m Sinitta's
Badges

400m Sinitta's
Character mask

Colour in your character mask. Then cut out and stick to a band of card, ready to place around your head.

400m Sinitta's
2 times table poem

400m Sinitta says 'How are you?
Run with me, there's lots to do.'
1 x 2 makes 2.

100, 200, 300 more,
2 lots of 2 equals 4.

Without cheating she knows all the tricks,
3 groups of 2 are 6.

To win the race, now that would be great,
4 x 2 equals 8.

But losing's OK every now and then
5 lots of 2 make 10.

Just try your best, that's all you can do
12 is the same as 6 x 2.

All that matters is that you stay really keen
7 lots of 2 make 14.

You can run so fast, that you're barely seen
8 groups of 2 are 16.

Practice makes perfect, you're a fast running
bean
9 x 2 makes 18.

You've done 400 metres – that is plenty,
10 x 2? That is 20.

But make sure you enjoy yourself too
11 x 2 is 22.

Otherwise you collapse to the floor!
12 x 2 makes 24!

400m Sinitta's 2 times table song

Tracks
● 17 & 30

400m Sinitta, she ran round the track
The ref shouted to her, for each lap you
score, you get 2 points.

400m Sinitta she ran round the track
She ran 1 lap and almost collapsed!
The ref shouted to her, 'What did you get?'
She said '2', so 1 x 2 must be 2.

400m Sinitta she ran round the track
She ran 2 laps and almost collapsed!
The ref shouted to her, 'What did you get?'
She said '4', so 2 x 2 must be 4.

Let's do more!

400m Sinitta she ran round the track
She ran 3 laps and almost collapsed!
The ref shouted to her, 'What did you get?'
She said '6', so 2 x 3 must be 6.

400m Sinitta she ran round the track
She ran 4 laps and almost collapsed!
The ref shouted to her, 'What did you get?'
She said '8', so 4 x 2 must be 8.

Wave to your mate!

400m Sinitta she ran round the track
She ran 5 laps and almost collapsed!
The ref shouted to her, 'What did you get?'
She said '10', so 5 x 2 must be 10.

400m Sinitta she ran round the track
She ran 6 laps and almost collapsed!
The ref shouted to her, 'What did you get?'
She said '12', so 6 x 2 must be 12.

Don't give up on yourself!

400m Sinitta she ran round the track
She ran 7 laps and almost collapsed!
The ref shouted to her, 'What did you get?'
She said '14', so 7 x 2 must be 14.

400m Sinitta she ran round the track
She ran 8 laps and almost collapsed!
The ref shouted to her, 'What did you get?'
She said '16', so 8 x 2 must be 16.

You're the best that we've seen!

400m Sinitta she ran round the track
She ran 9 laps and almost collapsed!
The ref shouted to her, 'What did you get?'
She said '18', so 9 x 2 must be 18.

400m Sinitta she ran round the track
She ran 10 laps and almost collapsed!
The ref shouted to her, 'What did you get?'
She said '20', so 10 x 2 must be 20.

Keep on going, you're up to 20!

400m Sinitta she ran round the track
She ran 11 laps and almost collapsed!
The ref shouted to her, 'What did you get?'
She said '22' so 11 x 2 is 22.

400m Sinitta she ran round the track
She ran 12 laps and almost collapsed!
The ref shouted to her 'What did you get?'
She said '24' so 12 x 2 is 24.

Wow! The great and good applause!

400m Sinitta's
2 times table
challenge

1 x 2 =	20 ÷ 2 =	8 x 2 =	2 x 9 =	10 ÷ 2 =
	2 x 4 =		12 x 2 =	
7 x 2 =		2 x 1 =		2 x 11 =
2 x 10 =	18 ÷ 2 =	2 x 2 =	10 x 2 =	
	6 ÷ 2 =		6 x 2 =	8 ÷ 2 =
2 x 5 =		12 ÷ 2 =		
2 ÷ 2 =	3 x 2 =		4 x 2 =	2 x 7 =
2 x 12 =	2 ÷ 1 =			
		2 x 6 =	5 x 2 =	22 ÷ 2 =
9 x 2 =	14 ÷ 2 =		2 x 8 =	6 x 2 =
24 ÷ 2 =	11 x 2 =	4 ÷ 2 =		2 x 3 =

400m Sinitta's
2 times table word problem challenge

1. Each of the 6 runners in the race drank 2 bottles of water. How many bottles were drunk altogether?

2. There are 4 runners in the team and they all ran 2 laps of the track. How many laps were run altogether?

3. There are 20 laps to be run and 10 runners to take part. How many laps must they each complete to keep the race fair?

4. How many laps would be run if 8 runners each ran 2 laps of the track?

5. If there were 7 athletes in each team and there are 2 teams, how many athletes are there altogether?

Long Jump Jim's 10 times table activities

1	×	**10**	=	10
2	×	**10**	=	20
3	×	**10**	=	30
4	×	**10**	=	40
5	×	**10**	=	50
6	×	**10**	=	60
7	×	**10**	=	70
8	×	**10**	=	80
9	×	**10**	=	90
10	×	**10**	=	100
11	×	**10**	=	110
12	×	**10**	=	120

Jump as far as you can down the garden, counting in 10s as you go!

Challenge your parent to a long jump challenge. Every time you jump the furthest, up your score by 10!

Throw a bean bag, then jump to it counting in 10s. Try again, seeing if you can throw further this time!

Write the numbers 1 to 12 lots of times all over your patio with chalk. Race a friend to the other side, by jumping onto numbers. You can only jump onto the next number when you have multiplied it by 10 and shouted the answer. Who will get there first?

Long Jump Jim's
10 times table

1	× **10**	=	10
2	× **10**	=	20
3	× **10**	=	30
4	× **10**	=	40
5	× **10**	=	50
6	× **10**	=	60
7	× **10**	=	70
8	× **10**	=	80
9	× **10**	=	90
10	× **10**	=	100
11	× **10**	=	110
12	× **10**	=	120

Long Jump Jim's Number fans

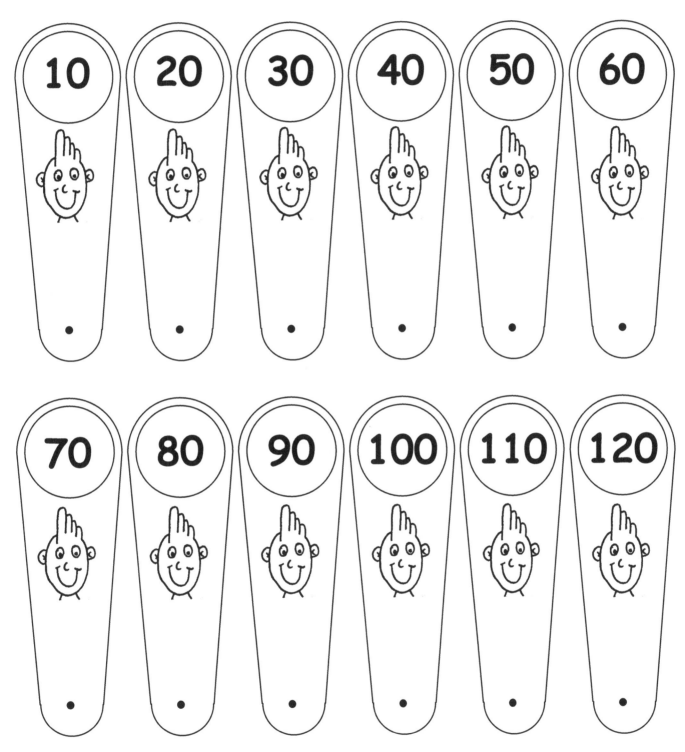

Long Jump Jim's
Visual grouping

10 x ___ = ____

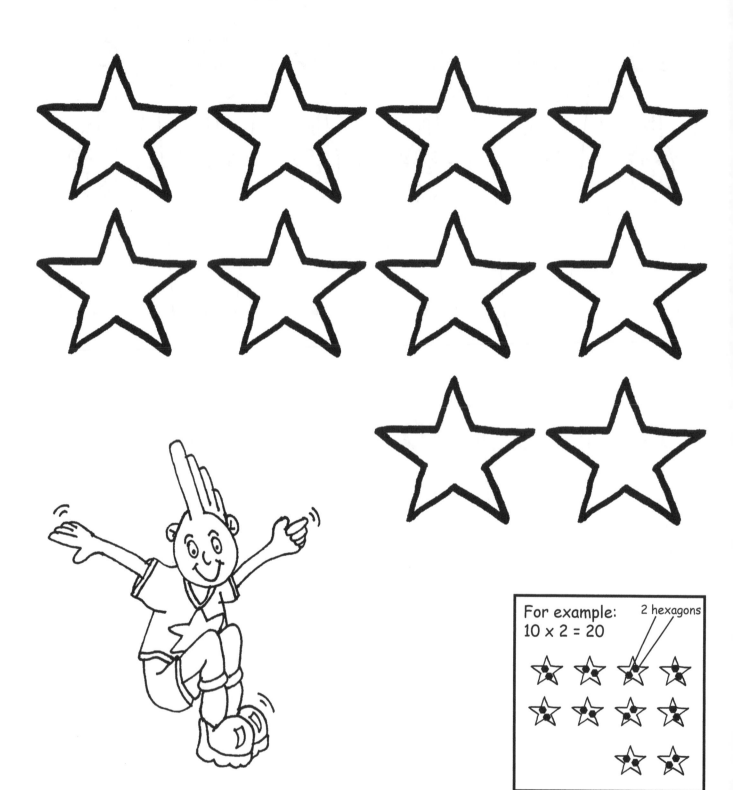

For example:
10 x 2 = 20   2 hexagons

Long Jump Jim's
Badges

Long Jump Jim's
Character mask

10 times table
Silver Award

Colour in your character mask. Then cut out and stick to a band of card, ready to place around your head.

Long Jump Jim's 10 times table poem

10 times table
Silver Award

Long Jump Jim says here we go again
1 x 10 is 10.

This isn't his first time, he's done it a plenty
2 lots of 10 make 20.

He flies through the sky – just like a bee
3 groups of 10 are 30.

It's a great jump, he's full of glee
4 x 10 equals 40.

Jim's jumped further than a flea
5 lots of 10 are 50.

He run and runs and jumps with glee
6 x 10 is 60.

Last jump now, it's number three
7 groups of 10 make 70.

Jim's getting hungry – he'd like his tea
8 lots of 10 are 80.

A long run up, that's the key
9 x 10 is 90.

Save the best until last, 10 metres dead
10 groups of 10 make 100.

He jumps all the way to the winning pen
11 lots of 10 are 110.

The crowds are cheering him a plenty
12 x 10 makes 120.

Long Jump Jim's
10 times table song

Chorus
Long Jump Jim is counting in 10s as he jumps
Long Jump Jim is counting in 10s as he jumps
Long Jump Jim is counting in 10s
Counting in 10s, counting in 10s as he jumps.

Singing 1 x 10 is 10 as he jumps
Singing 2 x 10 is 20 as he jumps
Singing 3 x 10 is 30
3 x 10 is 30, 3 x 10 is 30 as he jumps.

Long Jump Jim is counting chorus

Singing 4 x 10 is 40 as he leaps
Singing 5 x 10 is 50 as he leaps
Singing 6 x 10 is 60
6 x 10 is 60, 6 x 10 is 60 as he leaps.

Long Jump Jim is counting chorus

Singing 7 x 10 is 70 as he flies
Singing 8 x 10 is 80, as he flies
Singing 9 x 10 is 90
9 x 10 is 90, 9 x 10 is 90 as he flies.

Long Jump Jim is counting chorus

Singing 10 x 10 is 100 as he lands
Singing 11 x 10 is 110 as he lands
Singing 12 x 10 is 120
12 x 10 is 120, 12 x 10 is 120 as he lands.

Long Jump Jim is counting chorus

Long Jump Jim's 10 times table challenge

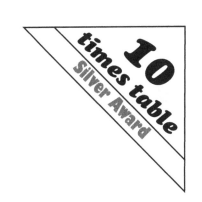

1 x 10 =	70 ÷ 10 =	4 x 10 =		10 ÷ 10 =
11 x 10 =	10 x 10 =		10 x 3 =	5 x 10 =
6 x 10 =		60 ÷ 10 =	120 ÷ 10 =	
	10 x 4 =	2 x 10 =	80 ÷ 10 =	10 x 1 =
10 x 2 =	20 ÷ 10 =		30 ÷ 10 =	
10 ÷ 10 =	10 x 6 =		7 x 10 =	10 x 7 =
3 x 10 =	110 ÷ 10 =	10 x 9 =		50 ÷ 10 =
100 ÷ 10 =	10 x 11 =		8 x 10 =	
10 x 12 =		90 ÷ 10 =		9 x 10 =
10 x 8 =	40 ÷ 10 =			12 x 10 =

Long Jump Jim's 10 times table word problem challenge

1. 10 people jump 2 metres. How many metres is that in total?

2. Long Jump Jim jumps 10 metres in 6 events. How many metres has he jumped altogether?

3. 60 metres has been jumped in total by 10 people. How many metres is that each?

4. 10 long jump champions receive 3 trophies each. How many trophies is that in total?

5. Long Jump Jim jumps 10 metres a day. How many metres does he jump in a week?

Javelin John's
5 times table activities

1	×	**5**	=	5
2	×	**5**	=	10
3	×	**5**	=	15
4	×	**5**	=	20
5	×	**5**	=	25
6	×	**5**	=	30
7	×	**5**	=	35
8	×	**5**	=	40
9	×	**5**	=	45
10	×	**5**	=	50
11	×	**5**	=	55
12	×	**5**	=	60

Make a javelin out of a kitchen roll. Write the numbers 1 to 12 on the drive. Throw your javelin and multiply by 5.

Throw your javelin down the garden. Count in 5s for every step you have to take to fetch it. See if you can beat your partner!

Throw your javelin to your friend and back counting in 5s.

Make a target board with the numbers 1 to 12 on it. Throw your javelin at it. Whatever number you land on, times it by 5. You and your teammates have 5 goes each, who has the biggest total?

Javelin John's
5 times table

1	×	**5**	=	5
2	×	**5**	=	10
3	×	**5**	=	15
4	×	**5**	=	20
5	×	**5**	=	25
6	×	**5**	=	30
7	×	**5**	=	35
8	×	**5**	=	40
9	×	**5**	=	45
10	×	**5**	=	50
11	×	**5**	=	55
12	×	**5**	=	60

Javelin John's
Number fans

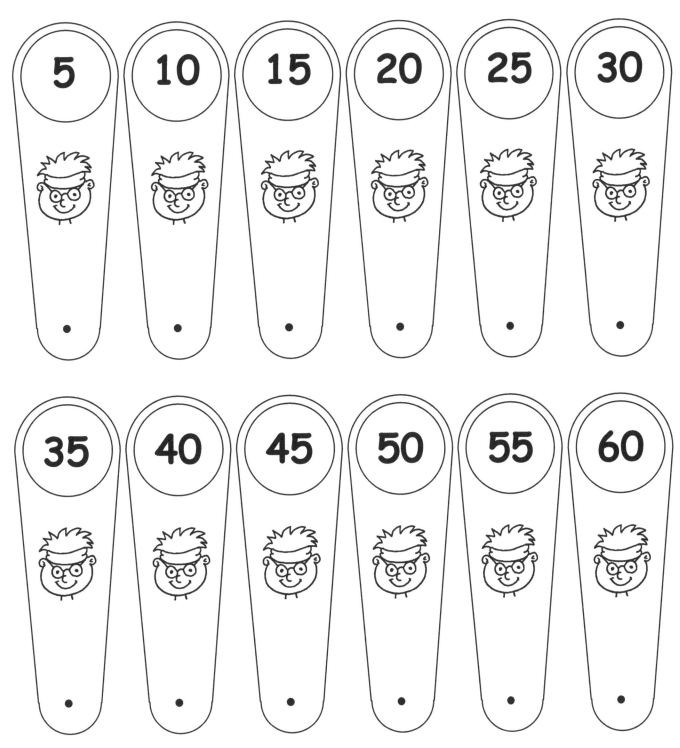

Javelin John's
Visual grouping

5 x ___ = ____

For example: 2 circles
5 x 2 = 10

Javelin John's
Badges

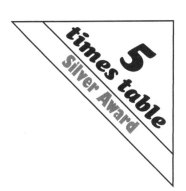

The Mighty Multiples Times Table Challenge

Javelin John's
Character mask

Colour in your character mask. Then cut out and stick to a band of card, ready to place around your head.

Javelin John's
5 times table poem

Javelin John is first to arrive
1 x 5 is 5.

Javelin John wants to score more than Ben
2 lots of 5 are 10.

Do you think he'll be in between?
3 x 5 makes 15.

He tries and tries with effort a plenty
4 x 5 equals 20.

He feels so happy, he does a dive
5 lots of 5 are 25.

The ground makes his clothes all dirty
6 groups of 5 are 30.

Back on the bus because he can't drive
7 x 5 is 35.

His Mum tells him off because he has been naughty
8 lots of 5 are 40.

It's bath then bed after tea at five
9 groups of 5 are 45.

He places his medal for all to see
10 x 5 is 50.

He can't wait to show his mate Clive
11 x 5 makes 55.

John hangs his medals in a tree
12 x 5 - that makes 60.

Javelin John's
5 times table song

Tracks
19 & 32

Javelin John he does a jive
While really trying to learn his 5s
1 x 5 is 5 (yeah) 1 x 5 is 5.

Javelin John he's got to 10
With 2 groups of 5 in his pen.
2 x 5 is 10 (yeah) 2 x 5 is 10.

Javelin John has reached 15
With 3 lots of 5, he's really keen
3 x 5 is 15 (yeah) 3 x 5's 15.

Javelin John he can see 20
Thinks 4 times 5, that's plenty
4 x 5 is 20 (yeah) 4 x 5's 20.

Javelin John he throws 25
5 groups of 5 give John high 5s.
5 x 5 is 25 (yeah) 5 x 5's 25.

Javelin John he makes 30
6 times 5 and he's really filthy.
6 x 5 is 30 (yeah) 6 x 5's 30.

Javelin John passes 35
7 times 5 makes him feel alive
7 x 5 is 35 (yeah) 7 x 5's 35.

Javelin John he aims for 40
With 8 lots of 5 that's real sporty
8 x 5 is 40 (yeah) 8 x 5 is 40.

Javelin John throws a big 45
On 9 lots of 5, he does thrive
9 x 5 is 45 (yeah) 9 x 5's 45.

Javelin John wants to reach 50
10 times 5 that's pretty nifty!
10 x 5 is 50 (yeah) 10 x 5's 50.

Javelin John eyes up 55
To 11 groups of 5 will be drive
11 x 5 is 55 (yeah) 11 x 5's 55.

Javelin John hits jackpot 60
12 lots of 6 put him top of the tree
12 x 5 is 60 (yeah) 12 x 5's 60!

Javelin John's 5 times table challenge

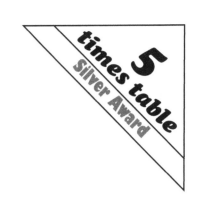

1 x 5 =	5 ÷ 1 =	5 x 1 =	4 x 5 =	15 ÷ 5 =
10 ÷ 5 =	2 x 5 =	60 ÷ 5 -	5 x 5 =	
5 x 2 =		5 x 10 =	6 x 5 =	11 x 5 =
5 x 11 =	20 ÷ 5 =			
30 ÷ 5 =		3 x 5 =	5 x 3 =	5 x 7 =
	35 ÷ 5 =			25 ÷ 5 =
7 x 5 =	5 x 8 =	40 ÷ 5 =	8 x 5 =	
55 ÷ 5 =			50 ÷ 5 =	5 x 4 =
45 ÷ 5 =	12 x 5 =	9 x 5 =		10 x 5 =
5 x 6 =		5 x 12 =	5 x 9 =	

Javelin John's
5 times table word problem challenge

1. John throws his javelin 5 metres, 7 times. How many metres has he thrown his javelin altogether?

2. Javelin John needs some sweets for energy! After each of the 6 events he eats 5 sweets. How many has he eaten in total?

3. Javelin John and his 4 friends each throw 2 javelins. How many javelins are thrown altogether?

4. Javelin John has 8 javelins and on each javelin there are 5 stickers. How many stickers are there in total?

5. Javelin John uses each of his 5 javelins, 5 times in 1 day. How many times has he thrown his javelin that day?

Freestyle Freda's
4 times table
activities

1	×	4	=	4
2	×	4	=	8
3	×	4	=	12
4	×	4	=	16
5	×	4	=	20
6	×	4	=	24
7	×	4	=	28
8	×	4	=	32
9	×	4	=	36
10	×	4	=	40
11	×	4	=	44
12	×	4	=	48

Write multiples of 4 on pebbles – drop them into the pool and dive down to get one. When you surface, think of the question to match your answer, eg if you pull up a 12, you say 3 x 4 is 12.

Write the answers to the 4 times tables on the bottom of your rubber ducks! Get somebody to ask you a question then choose a stroke to swim around your bath until you find your answer!

See how many times you can say your 4 times table before your bath fills up for bath time!

Visit your local swimming pool and sing your 4 times tables as you swim! See if you can get to 48 by the time you have swum a width!

Freestyle Freda's
4 times table

1	×	**4**	=	4
2	×	**4**	=	8
3	×	**4**	=	12
4	×	**4**	=	16
5	×	**4**	=	20
6	×	**4**	=	24
7	×	**4**	=	28
8	×	**4**	=	32
9	×	**4**	=	36
10	×	**4**	=	40
11	×	**4**	=	44
12	×	**4**	=	48

Freestyle Freda's
Number fans

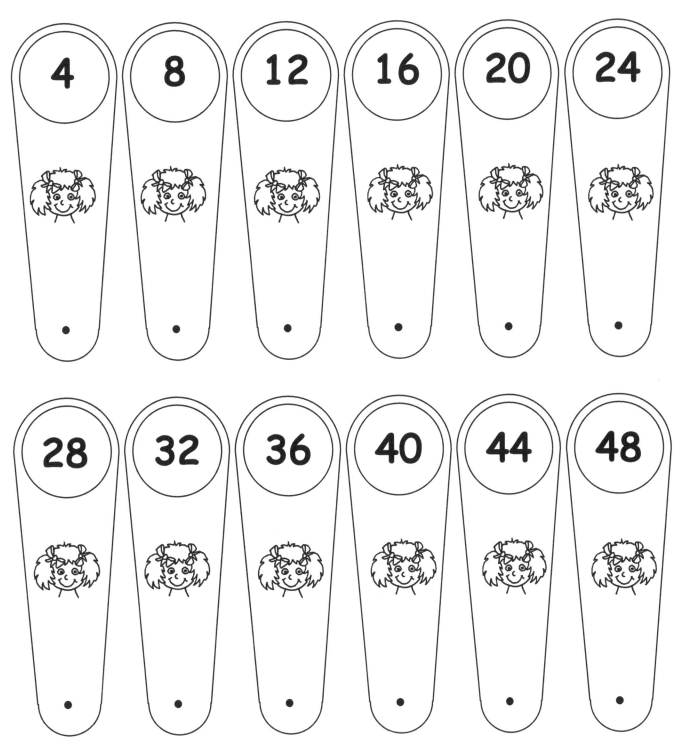

4   8   12   16   20   24

28   32   36   40   44   48

Freestyle Freda's
Visual grouping

4 x _____ = _____

For example:
4 x 2 = 8

2 triangles

Freestyle Freda's Badges

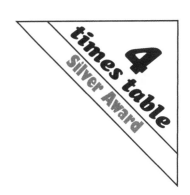

Freestyle Freda's
Character mask

Colour in your character mask. Then cut out and stick to a band of card, ready to place around your head.

Freestyle Freda's
4 times table poem

Track
7

Freestyle Freda rushes through the door
We all know 1 x 4 is 4.

Freestyle Freda is running late
2 lots of 4 make 8.

She has to get ready by herself
3 groups of 4 are 12.

She gets to her lane, cheered on by the team
4 x 4 is 16.

Experience at this she has aplenty
5 lots of 4 are 20.

She dives in the water, splashes galore
6 groups of 4 are 24.

She's swimming so fast, she's doing great
7 x 4 is 28.

Only one last length is left to do
8 lots of 4 are 32.

The press are taking lots of pics
9 groups of 4 are 36.

She is the fastest, we all can see
10 times 4 is 40.

Every race her skills grow more
11 x 4 is 44.

Now Freestyle Freda is just so great
12 x 4 is 48.

Freestyle Freda's
4 times table song

Tracks
20 & 33

Chorus
Oh Freestyle Freda,
Oh Freestyle Freda,
Oh Freestyle Freda,
Freda knows just what the 4s are about!

She times 1 by 4, then she swims some more
Easy peasy, she knows that it makes 4
She has 2 lots of 4, which equals 8
Well done Freda you really flew!

Oh Freestyle Freda chorus

She times 3 by 4, then she swims some more
Easy peasy, she knows that it makes 12
She has 4 lots of 4, which equals 16
Well done Freda you really flew!

Oh Freestyle Freda chorus

She times 5 by 4, then she swims some more
Easy peasy, she knows that it makes 20.
She has 6 lots of 4, which equals 24
Well done Freda you really flew!

Oh Freestyle Freda chorus

She times 7 by 4, then she swims some more
Easy peasy, she knows that it makes 28.
She has 8 lots of 4, which equals 32
Well done Freda you really flew!

Oh Freestyle Freda chorus

She times 9 by 4, then she swims some more
Easy peasy, she knows it makes 36
She has 10 lots of 4, which equals 40
Well done Freda you really flew!

Oh Freestyle Freda chorus

She times 11 by 4, then she swims some more
Easy peasy, she knows it makes 44
She has 12 lots of 4, which equals 48
Well done Freda you really flew!

Oh Freestyle Freda chorus

Sung to the tune of the 'Hokey Cokey'.

Freestyle Freda's
4 times table challenge

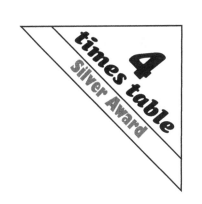

1 x 4 =	4 x 1 =	8 ÷ 4 =	3 x 4 =	4 x 10 =
4 ÷ 4 =		4 x 2 =		12 ÷ 4 =
4 x 4 =	4 x 3 =	16 ÷ 4 =	11 x 4 =	5 x 4 =
	12 x 4 =			
20 ÷ 4 =		2 x 4 =	4 x 12 =	4 x 9 =
6 x 4 =	24 ÷ 4 =		28 ÷ 4 =	44 ÷ 4 =
	4 x 11 =	7 x 4 =		8 x 4 =
9 x 4 =		4 ÷ 1 =	4 x 6 =	
48 ÷ 4 =	10 x 4 =			32 ÷ 4 =
4 x 8 =	4 x 5 =	36 ÷ 4 =	40 ÷ 4 =	4 x 7 =

Freestyle Freda's
4 times table word problem challenge

1. If 4 swimmers swim 3 lengths each, how many lengths are swum altogether?

2. If there are 5 races and each has 4 swimmers, how many swimmers are there in total?

3. If the race is 40 metres long and there are 4 swimmers how many metres do they each have to swim, in order to split the 40 metres equally between them?

4. How many metres would it be altogether if 8 people each swam 4 metres?

5. If Freda entered 4 races, each of 4 lengths, how many lengths would she have swum in total?

Mighty Multiples
Silver Award

Congratulations!

Awarded to

_____

On

_____

You have successfully completed the following awards:

400m
Sinitta

Javelin
John

Long Jump
Jim

Freestyle
Freda

High Jump Heather's
3 times table activities

1	×	**3**	=	3
2	×	**3**	=	6
3	×	**3**	=	9
4	×	**3**	=	12
5	×	**3**	=	15
6	×	**3**	=	18
7	×	**3**	=	21
8	×	**3**	=	24
9	×	**3**	=	27
10	×	**3**	=	30
11	×	**3**	=	33
12	×	**3**	=	36

Jump around your garden chanting your 3 times tables – how far can you get?

Stick numbers 1-36 across the wall. Jump up high and grab all multiples of 3!

Get somebody to count to 100. Every time you hear a multiple of 3, jump as high as you can.

Draw numbers all over your patio with chalk. See if you can find a track to the other side only stepping on multiples of 3.

High Jump Heather's
3 times table

$$1 \times 3 = 3$$
$$2 \times 3 = 6$$
$$3 \times 3 = 9$$
$$4 \times 3 = 12$$
$$5 \times 3 = 15$$
$$6 \times 3 = 18$$
$$7 \times 3 = 21$$
$$8 \times 3 = 24$$
$$9 \times 3 = 27$$
$$10 \times 3 = 30$$
$$11 \times 3 = 33$$
$$12 \times 3 = 36$$

High Jump Heather's Number fans

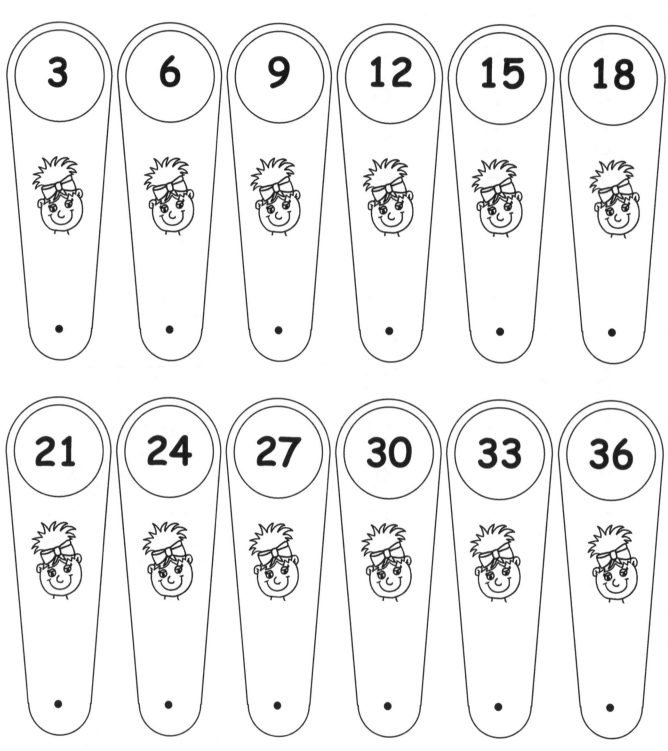

High Jump Heather's
Visual grouping

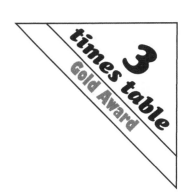
$3 \times \underline{\hspace{1cm}} = \underline{\hspace{1.5cm}}$

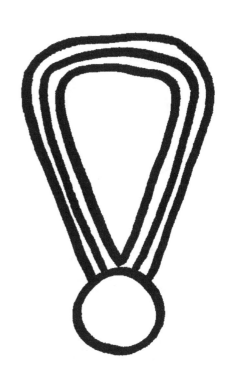

For example:
$3 \times 2 = 6$

2 triangles

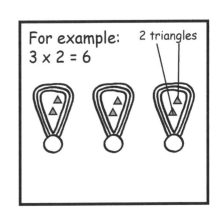

High Jump Heather's Badges

High Jump Heather's
Character mask

Colour in your character mask. Then cut out and stick to a band of card, ready to place around your head.

High Jump Heather's
3 times table poem

High Jump Heather's jump lands in a tree!
We all know 1 x 3 equals 3.

High Jump Heather is now in a fix
2 groups of 3 make 6.

She's not hurt, she's doing fine
3 lots of 3 are 9.

She stands on branches, just like shelves
3 x 4 is 12.

It's the funniest thing her friends have ever seen
5 groups of 3 are 15.

They all help her, as a team
6 lots of 3 make 18.

They make a tower, one by one
7 x 3 is 21.

High Jump Heather climbs down to the floor
8 x 3 is 24.

Just in time, her event's at 11
9 groups of 3 make 27.

Off she sets 1, 2, 3
10 times 3 is 30!

Flying through the air, she's the jumping queen
11 times 3 makes 33.

She jumps so high, the crowds take pics!
12 times 3 equals 36.

High Jump Heather's
3 times table song

3 times table
Gold Award

Tracks
21 & 34

High Jump Heather loves to count
1 x 3 is 3 she shouts.

2 x 3 that's 6 she says
I'm always counting in my head.

3 x 3 equals 9
Counting sends tingles up my spine.

4 x 3 that's 12 you see
Count on with me if you please.

5 x 3 well that's easy
We can see it makes 15.

3 x 6 makes 18
I can count jumping merrily.

7 x 3 equals 21
Count with me, I won't be the only one.

8 x 3 is 24
Keep on counting there aren't many more.

9 x 3 that's 27
Now I'm really in counting heaven.

10 x 3 well that's thirty
Well I think that's nearly plenty.

11 x 3 equals 33
Jumping makes Heather fly free.

12 x 3 makes 36
Heather and jumping are a fab mix.

High Jump Heather counts in 3s
Count with her, it is easy!

Sung to the tune of 'Twinkle, twinkle little star'.

High Jump Heather's 3 times table challenge

1 x 3 =	24 ÷ 3 =	8 x 3 =	3 x 9 =	18 ÷ 3 =
	3 x 4 =	5 x 3 =		3 ÷ 1 =
7 x 3 =			21 ÷ 3 =	11 x 3 =
3 x 10 =	27 ÷ 3 =	2 x 3 =	10 x 3 =	
	30 ÷ 3 =			30 ÷ 3 =
3 x 5 =		9 ÷ 3 =	12 x 3 =	
6 ÷ 3 =	3 x 2 =		4 x 3 =	3 x 7 =
	3 x 1 =			
3 x 11 =		3 x 6 =		3 x 12 =
9 x 3 =	15 ÷ 3 =	36 ÷ 3 =	3 x 8 =	6 x 3 =
3 ÷ 3 =		12 ÷ 3 =		3 x 3 =

High Jump Heather's 3 times table word problem challenge

1. Each of the 5 high jumpers, jump 3 metres high. How many metres did they jump altogether?

2. There are 3 high jumpers and they each require 4 bottles of water a day. How many bottles do they require altogether each day?

3. If 3 people jumped 7 metres, how many metres would that be altogether?

4. How many metres would it be altogether if 6 people jumped 3 metres?

5. If there were 8 events in the high jumping section of the event and each event had their own bronze, silver and gold certificates for the winners, how many certificates must I have ready to cover all 8 events?

Backstroke Brenda's
6 times table activities

1	×	**6**	=	6
2	×	**6**	=	12
3	×	**6**	=	18
4	×	**6**	=	24
5	×	**6**	=	30
6	×	**6**	=	36
7	×	**6**	=	42
8	×	**6**	=	48
9	×	**6**	=	54
10	×	**6**	=	60
11	×	**6**	=	66
12	×	**6**	=	72

Walk backwards counting in 6s. How far can you get without bumping into something?

How many widths of back stroke can you swim by the time you have counted to 72 in 6s? Challenge your friends too.

Can you put all your clothes on back to front whilst counting in sixes?

At bath time, can you say your whole 6 times table before your bath is full?

Backstroke Brenda's
6 times table

1	×	6	=	6
2	×	6	=	12
3	×	6	=	18
4	×	6	=	24
5	×	6	=	30
6	×	6	=	36
7	×	6	=	42
8	×	6	=	48
9	×	6	=	54
10	×	6	=	60
11	×	6	=	66
12	×	6	=	72

Backstroke Brenda's
Number fans

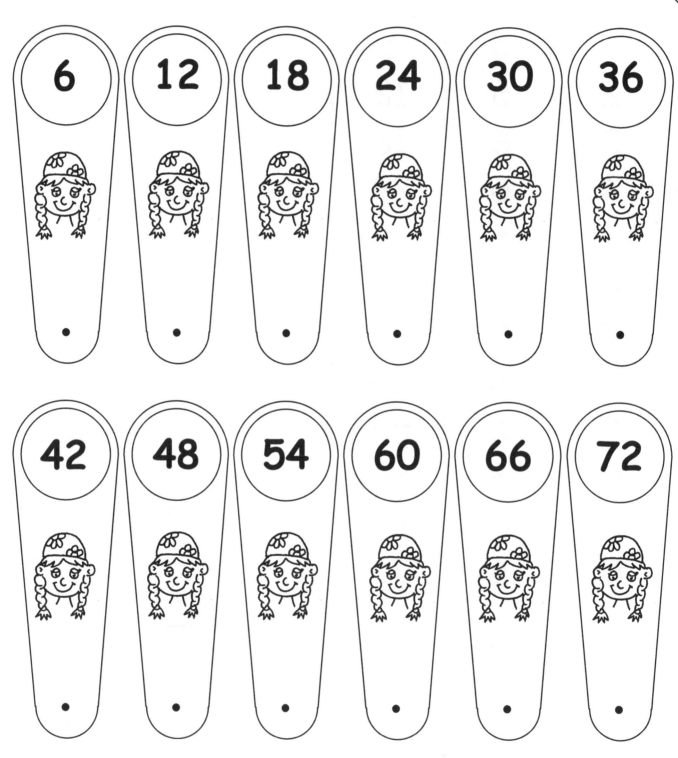

6   12   18   24   30   36

42   48   54   60   66   72

Backstroke Brenda's
Visual grouping

6 x ____ = _____

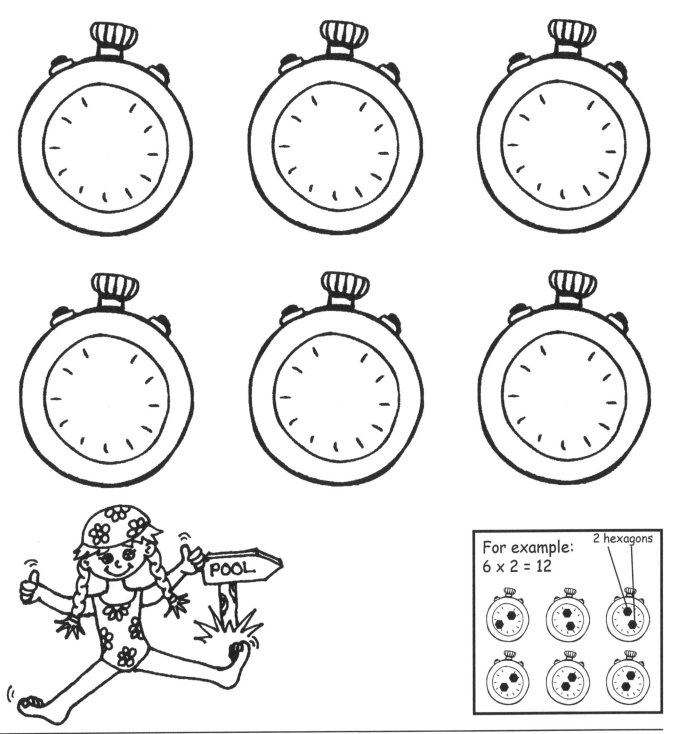

For example:
6 x 2 = 12

2 hexagons

Backstroke Brenda's Badges

Backstroke Brenda's
Character mask

Colour in your character mask. Then cut out and stick to a band of card, ready to place around your head.

Backstroke Brenda's
6 times table poem

Track
9

Will it be lucky Brenda's in lane 6?
1 x 6 is 6.

Into the water her arms do delve
2 lots of 6 are 12.

She really has the swimming gene
3 groups of 6 make 18.

The crowds cheer her more and more
4 times 6 is 24.

In all this water, she's still thirsty
5 lots of 6 are 30.

Using arms and legs is a real good mix
6 groups of 6 make 36.

Gliding through the water, she just flew
7 x 6 is 42.

The crowd starts singing, 'You're really great'
8 groups of 6 make 48.

She's nearly finished, just half a length more
9 times 6 is 54.

She's finished first, as happy as can be
10 lots of 6 make 60.

Come on Brenda – quick, quick, quick
Yes, 11 x 6 is 66.

The trophy's hers, as we always knew
12 x 6 is 72.

Backstroke Brenda's
6 times table song

Tracks
22 & 35

Chorus
Backstroke Brenda, she is a really good swimmer
Backstroke Brenda, she used to be a beginner
Backstroke Brenda, she's going to be a winner
Backstroke Brenda, and you can be a winner too.

When she's in the pool and she's in a race,
She will always try to get that first place,
1 x 6, that's the same as 6
Brenda always tries to do her best!

2 x 6 that equals 12
3 x 6 that equals 18
4 x 6 that equals 24
Four, four, four, let's do some more!

Backstroke Brenda chorus

5 x 6 equals 30
All this water around and Brenda's still thirsty
6 x 6, well that equals 36
The cameras go click, taking lots of pictures.

7 x 6 that equals 42
8 x 6 equals 48
9 x 6 equals 54
Four, four, four, let's do some more!

Backstroke Brenda chorus

Now Brenda, she is doing fine.
With the end in sight, she can see the finish line,
One last push and she'll have won
Brenda keep going, you are nearly there!

10 x 6 that equals 60!
11 x 6 that equals 66
12 x 6 that equals 72
Well done Brenda you really flew!

Backstroke Brenda chorus

Backstroke Brenda's 6 times table challenge

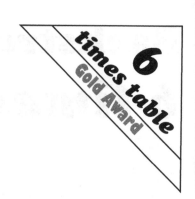

1 x 6 =	6 x 1 =	6 x 9 =	12 ÷ 6 =	3 x 6 =
6 x 5 =	2 x 6 =	18 ÷ 6 =	6 x 2 =	
42 ÷ 6 =			6 ÷ 6 =	48 ÷ 6 =
6 x 12 =	54 ÷ 6 =	8 x 6 =	6 x 11 =	6 x 6 =
5 x 6 =			24 ÷ 6 =	
	10 x 6 =	60 ÷ 6 =		6 x 4 =
30 ÷ 6 =		72 ÷ 6 =	4 x 6 =	
7 x 6 =	11 x 6 =	6 x 3 =		6 x 10 =
			66 ÷ 6 =	9 x 6 =
6 x 8 =	6 ÷ 1 =	36 ÷ 6 =	6 x 7 =	12 x 6 =

Backstroke Brenda's
6 times table word problem challenge

1. Brenda swims 6 lengths in 2 races. How many lengths has she swum altogether?

2. Brenda needs to swim 60 lengths a week in training. If she takes 1 day off a week, how many lengths must she swim on every other day of the week?

3. Brenda wears a new pair of flip flops to the pool for each race! In one day she swam 6 races. How many flip flops did she wear in total that day?

4. Brenda swims 6 lengths of back stroke 4 times a day. How many lengths does she swim in total a day?

5. The width of the pool is 6 metres. If Brenda swims 9 widths, how many metres has she swum?

Cycling Susie's
7 times table activities

1	×	7	=	7
2	×	7	=	14
3	×	7	=	21
4	×	7	=	28
5	×	7	=	35
6	×	7	=	42
7	×	7	=	49
8	×	7	=	56
9	×	7	=	63
10	×	7	=	70
11	×	7	=	77
12	×	7	=	84

Use elastic bands to hang number cards (1-12) to objects around your garden or in the park. Race your friend to collect as many numbers as you can. But, before you can take a number, you have to multiply it by 7 and shout the answer!

Attach numbers to objects around your garden, then time yourself to see how long it takes you to cycle around and collect all the multiples of 7.

Cycle to the shops counting in 7s the whole way there and back.

Put all of the multiples of 7 on cards on the floor around a big space. Make sure they are muddled up. Cycle to the cards in order, starting with 1 x 7 and ending with 12 x 7. How long did it take? Can somebody beat your time?

Cycling Susie's
7 times table

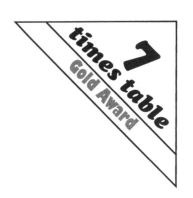

1	×	7	=	7
2	×	7	=	14
3	×	7	=	21
4	×	7	=	28
5	×	7	=	35
6	×	7	=	42
7	×	7	=	49
8	×	7	=	56
9	×	7	=	63
10	×	7	=	70
11	×	7	=	77
12	×	7	=	84

Cycling Susie's
Number fans

7 times table Gold Award

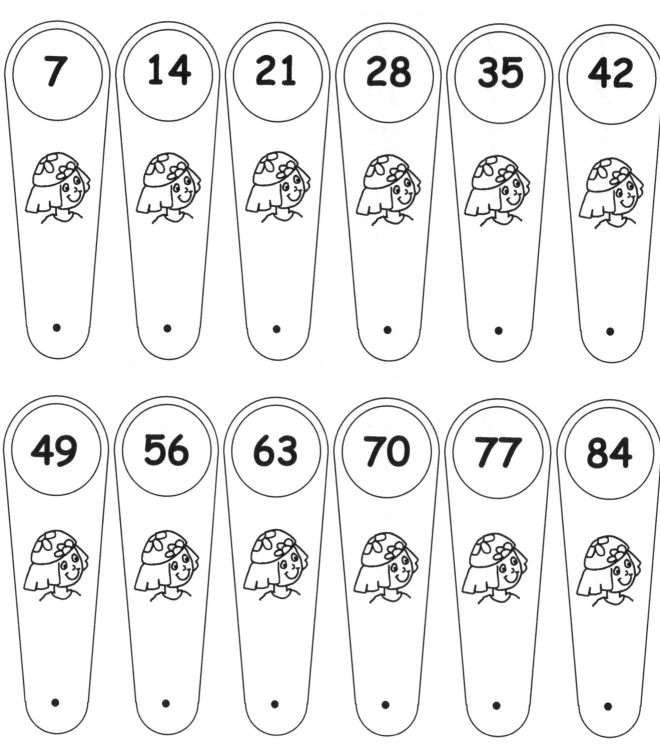

7   14   21   28   35   42

49   56   63   70   77   84

Cycling Susie's
Visual grouping

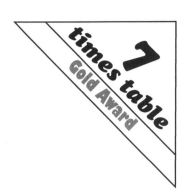

7 × ___ = _____

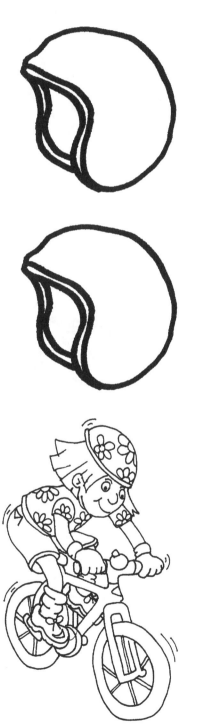

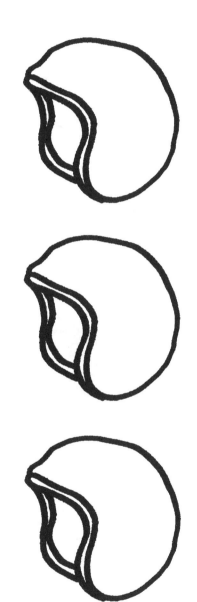

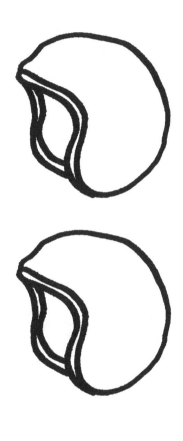

For example:
7 × 2 = 14   2 triangles

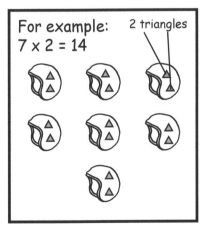

Cycling Susie's
Badges

7 times table Gold Award

Cycling Susie's
Character mask

Colour in your character mask. Then cut out and stick to a band of card, ready to place around your head.

Cycling Susie's
7 times table poem

Track
10

Cycling Susie rides up from Devon
1 x 7 equals 7.

Cycling Susie meets up with the team
2 lots of 7 are 14.

Susie and the team have so much fun
3 groups of 7 make 21.

Go, go Susie, you're so great
4 x 7 is 28.

Susie cycles, she doesn't drive
5 lots of 7 are 35.

It's the start of the race, she's all to do
6 groups of 7 are 42.

With 7 laps gone, she is doing fine
7 x 7 is 49.

Still going strong, she's still in the mix
8 lots of 7 make 56.

She crosses the finish line, 'Yippee!'
9 groups of 7 are 63.

Home on the bike in time for tea
10 x 7 is 70.

She sure is in winning heaven
11 x 7 is 77.

Susie has won trophies galore
12 x 7 is 84.

Cycling Susie's
7 times table song

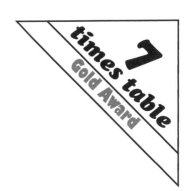

Tracks
23 & 36

Chorus
Keep on cycling, you're going really fast
Keep on speeding, learning 7s is so much fun
Susie and times 7 is a match made in heaven
Susie and times 7 just speed along

1 x 7 is 7, 2 x 7 is 14
She's the fastest girl on a bike that you've ever seen
3 x 7 is 21, 4 x 7 is 28
Keep on Susie, you're doing well, you're doing great!

Keep on cycling chorus

5 x 7 is 35, 6 x 7 is 42
Susie's doing this really well and so can you
7 7s is 49, 8 x 7 is 56
Cycling Susie is doing great, using all her tricks!

Keep on cycling chorus

9 x 7 is 63, 10 x 7 is 70
Susie's on the final lap, let's all give a clap.
11 7s are 77, 12 x 7 is 84
Susie wins, let's all applaud.

Keep on cycling chorus

Cycling Susie's 7 times table challenge

1 x 7 =	7 x 1 =	8 x 7 =	7 ÷ 1 =	4 x 7 =
14 ÷ 7 =	7 x 7 =		56 ÷ 7 =	7 ÷ 7 =
	70 ÷ 7 =	7 x 2 =		7 x 3 =
63 ÷ 7 =		7 x 11 =	2 x 7 =	
3 x 7 =	84 ÷ 7 =			10 x 7 =
	6 x 7 =	9 x 7 =	7 x 5 =	
35 ÷ 7 =		12 x 7 =	21 ÷ 7 =	28 ÷ 7 =
7 x 4 =	5 x 7 =			77 ÷ 7 =
7 x 12 =		11 x 7 =	7 x 6 =	
7 x 9 =	42 ÷ 7 =	7 x 10 =	49 ÷ 7 =	7 x 8 =

Cycling Susie's
7 times table word problem challenge

1.   There are 7 bikes in the race. How many wheels are there in total?

2.   There are 12 people in the race and each cycles 7 laps. How many laps is that in total?

3.   If Susie cycles 10 laps in 70 seconds, how many seconds does each lap take her?

4.   Susie and her 7 team mates each race 7 laps. How many laps long is the race?

5.   Susie cycles 9 miles in training, every day of the week. How many miles does she cycle a week?

Triple Jump Tracey's 8 times table activities

1	×	**8**	=	8
2	×	**8**	=	16
3	×	**8**	=	24
4	×	**8**	=	32
5	×	**8**	=	40
6	×	**8**	=	48
7	×	**8**	=	56
8	×	**8**	=	64
9	×	**8**	=	72
10	×	**8**	=	80
11	×	**8**	=	88
12	×	**8**	=	96

Get a sturdy bench or step. Jump on and off it while counting in 8s. How quickly can you do it?

Attach numbers to objects around your garden, then race a friend to jump round the garden to collect as many multiples of 8 as you can!

How many times can you jump up and down by the time you have completed your 8 times table?

Get 2 friends and race them round the garden, chanting the 8 times table as you jump

Triple Jump Tracey's
8 times table

1	×	**8**	=	8
2	×	**8**	=	16
3	×	**8**	=	24
4	×	**8**	=	32
5	×	**8**	=	40
6	×	**8**	=	48
7	×	**8**	=	56
8	×	**8**	=	64
9	×	**8**	=	72
10	×	**8**	=	80
11	×	**8**	=	88
12	×	**8**	=	96

Triple Jump Tracey's
Number fans

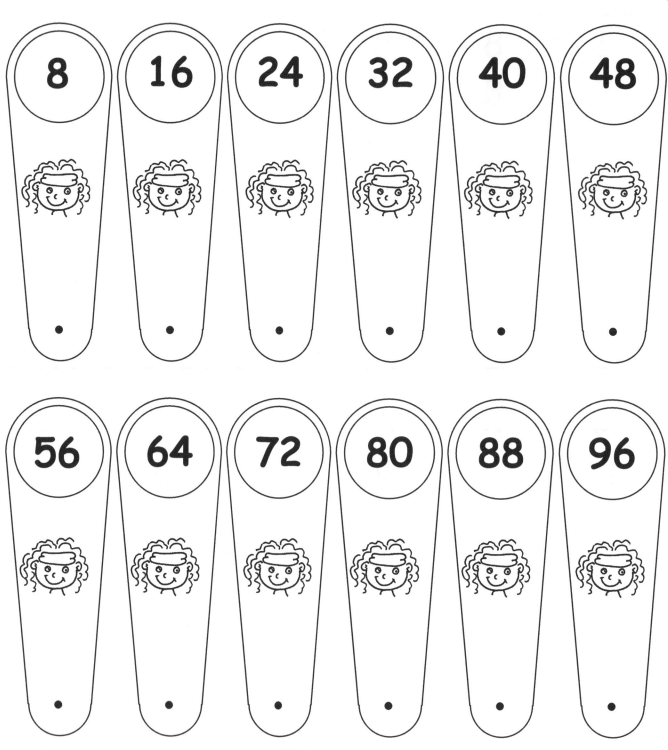

8 16 24 32 40 48

56 64 72 80 88 96

Triple Jump Tracey's
Visual grouping

8 x ___ = ____

For example:
8 x 2 = 16

2 hexagons

Triple Jump Tracey's
Badges

Triple Jump Tracey's
Character mask

Colour in your character mask. Then cut out and stick to a band of card, ready to place around your head.

Triple Jump Tracey's
8 times table poem

8 times table
Gold Award

Track
11

Triple Jump Tracey is feeling great
1 x 8 is 8.

Triple Jump Tracey is really keen
2 lots of 8 make 16.

Triple Jump Tracey jumps high off the floor
3 groups of 8 are 24.

Triple Jump Tracey knows what to do
4 x 8 is 32.

With a hop, skip, jump, 1, 2, 3
5 lots of 8 are 40.

Her longest jump was 6.8
6 groups of 8 are 48.

She wins the contest, but then feels sick
7 x 8 is 56.

She waves to the crowd and they clap galore
8 lots of 8 are 64.

She makes her way home with no more to do
9 groups of 8 are 72.

Before she leaves they thank her greatly
10 x 8 is 80.

She says goodbye to her best mate.
11 x 8 is 88.

Competition's hard when Tracey's in the mix
12 x 8 is 96.

Triple Jump Tracey's 8 times table song

Tracks
24 & 37

Chorus
Triple Jump Tracey likes to learn her 8s
Triple Jump Tracey likes to sing it with her mates.
Jumping up, jumping down,
Tracey's jumping all the time.
Come and sing along with me to our 8 times table rhyme.

With a run, skip and jump, Tracey tries her best
'Cause learning her tables is such a hard test.
But with lots of hard work,
And singing along
We'll find the best way is by singing this song!

1 x 8 is 8 and 2 is 16
And if you times it by 3 you score 24.

Triple Jump Tracey chorus

4 x 8 that makes 32
And if you times it by 5, you get 40.

Triple Jump Tracey chorus

With a run, skip and jump, Tracey tries her best
'Cause learning her tables is such a hard test.
But with lots of hard work,
And singing along
We'll find the best way is by singing this song!

6 x 8's 48, 7 x 8 is 56
And if you times it by 8 you score 64!

Triple Jump Tracey chorus

9 x 8's 72 and 10 8s are 80
We have lots of fun singing along with Tracey.

Triple Jump Tracey chorus

With a run, skip and jump, Tracey tries her best
'Cause learning her tables is such a hard test.
But with lots of hard work,
And singing along
We'll find the best way is by singing this song!

11 x 8 is 88 and 12 x 8 is 96
Oh when singing the 8s she's never in a mix.

Triple Jump Tracey chorus

Triple Jump Tracey's 8 times table challenge

1 x 8 =	8 x 1 =	16 ÷ 8 =	8 x 3 =	72 ÷ 8 =
8 ÷ 1 =	2 x 8 =			5 x 8 =
64 ÷ 8 =	11 x 8 =	8 x 2 =	32 ÷ 8 =	
				8 x 7 =
4 x 8 =	8 x 4 =	24 ÷ 8 =	3 x 8 =	88 ÷ 8 =
	8 x 11 =			8 x 8 =
8 x 6 =	6 x 8 =	8 x 9 =	48 ÷ 8 =	
8 x 12 =			7 x 8 =	40 ÷ 8 =
9 x 8 =	96 ÷ 8 =	8 ÷ 8 =	12 x 8 =	8 x 5 =
	8 x 10 =	10 x 8 =	56 ÷ 8 =	80 ÷ 8 =

Triple Jump Tracey's 8 times table word problem challenge

1. Tracey jumps 8 metres in 3 events. How many metres is that in total?

2. Tracey drinks 8 energy drinks a day. How many energy drinks is that in total in a 7 day week?

3. Tracey and her partner jump 16 metres between them in an event. They both jumped the same distance. How far did they jump each?

4. 8 people jump 80 metres between them. If they all jumped the same distance, how many metres did they jump each?

5. 8 people each jump 8 metres. How many metres were jumped altogether in that event?

Shot Put Tony's 9 times table activities

1	×	**9**	=	9
2	×	**9**	=	18
3	×	**9**	=	27
4	×	**9**	=	36
5	×	**9**	=	45
6	×	**9**	=	54
7	×	**9**	=	63
8	×	**9**	=	72
9	×	**9**	=	81
10	×	**9**	=	90
11	×	**9**	=	99
12	×	**9**	=	108

Make a target pad (with numbers 1 to 12 on it). Throw a ball and whatever you hit, you must multiply it by 9.

Count in 9s while throwing balls as far down the garden as possible. As you count higher, try and throw further!

Throw a ball to your partner while counting in 9s.

Throw balls into a bin – how many can you get in by the time you count to 108 in 9s?

Shot Put Tony's
9 times table

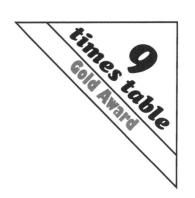

1	×	**9**	=	9
2	×	**9**	=	18
3	×	**9**	=	27
4	×	**9**	=	36
5	×	**9**	=	45
6	×	**9**	=	54
7	×	**9**	=	63
8	×	**9**	=	72
9	×	**9**	=	81
10	×	**9**	=	90
11	×	**9**	=	99
12	×	**9**	=	108

Shot Put Tony's
Number fans

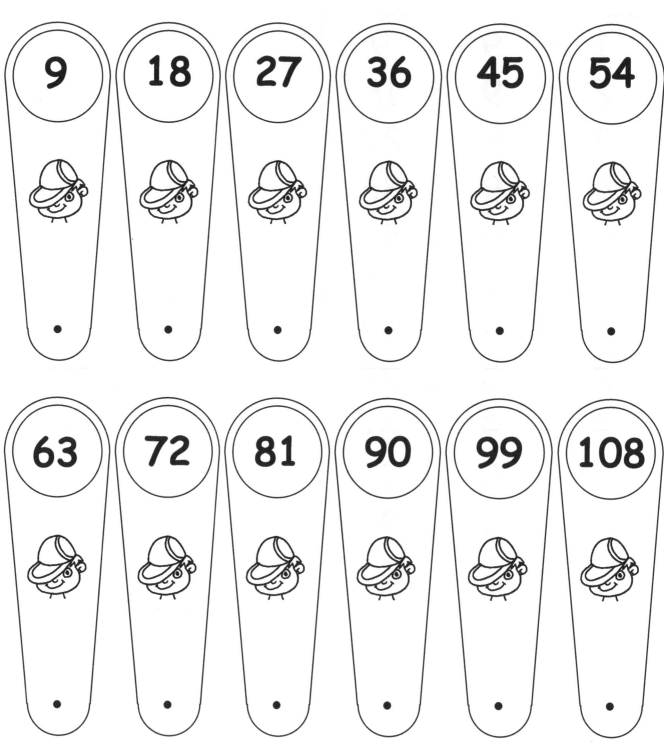

Shot Put Tony's
Visual grouping

9 x _____ = _____

For example:
9 x 2 = 18

2 circles

Shot Put Tony's Badges

Shot Put Tony's
Character mask

Colour in your character mask. Then cut out and stick to a band of card, ready to place around your head.

Shot Put Tony's
9 times table poem

Track
12

Shot put Tony is feeling fine
1 x 9 is 9.

Tony is the strongest we've ever seen!
2 x 9, that's 18.

When playing shot put, Tony's in heaven
3 x 9 is 27.

Shot put and Tony are a fantastic mix
4 lots of 9 are 36.

Playing shot put makes him come alive
9 x 5 is 45.

He strives to beat his top score!
9 groups of 6 make 54.

Playing shot put really fills him with glee
9 x 7 makes 63.

Out of the arena his shot put flew
8 lots of 9 make 72.

Oh the crowds cheered, because he had won
9 x 9 is 81.

The cheering crowds make him feel mighty
10 x 9, well, that is 90.

By now Tony's feeling mighty fine
11 x 9 is 99.

The best cheers are from his mates
12 x 9 is 108.

Shot Put Tony's
9 times table song

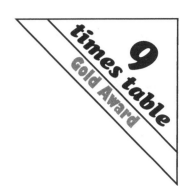

Tracks
25 & 38

Shot put Tony was learning his 9s
He wanted to do it without having to mime
So his wise old mum said to him
If you really want to be the best,
You've got to put yourself to the test.

1 x 9 is 9
2 x 9 is 18
3 x 9 is 27

If you really want to reach the shot put heaven
If you really want to be the best that can be
You really need to stick with me.

I said 4 x 9 is 36
5 x 9 is 45
6 x 9 is 54

If you really want to learn some more
To really be able to beat your score
You've got to come knocking at my door.

7 times 9 is 63
8 times 9 is 72
I said 9 times 9 is 81

So have you stopped feeling so blue?
Have you started to have a clue?
Because you know that you can do it too.

I said 10 x 9 is 90
11 x 9 is 99
12 x 9 is 108

Learning tables with Tony and you'll never be late
He might even become one of your best mates.

Now you've learnt your 9 times table
We hope you're feeling mighty
Even if it's ever so slightly!

Shot Put Tony's 9 times table challenge

1 x 9 =	9 x 1 =	10 x 9 =	9 ÷ 1 =	27 ÷ 9 =
	18 ÷ 9 =		9 x 2 =	6 x 9 =
7 x 9 =	9 x 4 =	3 x 9 =	9 x 11 =	
99 ÷ 9 =	9 x 5 =		45 ÷ 9 =	9 x 3 =
12 x 9 =	2 x 9 =	36 ÷ 9 =		72 ÷ 9 =
9 x 6 =	9 x 12 =	54 ÷ 9 =	9 x 11 =	9 ÷ 9 =
	81 ÷ 9 =	9 x 10 =	9 x 7 =	5 x 9 =
9 x 5 =			90 ÷ 9 =	
9 x 7 =	11 x 9 =	4 x 9 =	9 x 12 =	8 x 9 =
63 ÷ 9 =	9 x 8 =	9 x 8 =	9 x 9 =	108 ÷ 9 =

90M

Shot Put Tony's
9 times table word problem challenge

1. Each of the 6 competitors in the event threw 9 shot puts. How many shot puts were there to collect at the end?

2. To win their events Tony and his 4 team mates have, between them, to throw their shot puts a total of 45 metres. How many metres must they each throw their shot put equally to achieve this?

3. Each of the 9 competitors eats 6 energy sweets a day. How many is that in total each day?

4. There are 9 people who throw their shot puts 7 metres. How many metres is that altogether?

5. 81 people enter to throw their shot puts in an event. There can only be 9 people in each section. How many sections will I need, to allow everyone to enter?

Mighty Multiples
How to do the squares

400m Sinitta can give no more
'Cause 2 groups of 2 are four.

High Jump Heather is doing fine
'Cause 3 x 3 equals 9.

Freestyle Freda is the swimming queen
So remember 4 lots of 4 make 16.

Javelin John strives and strives
5 groups of 5 make 25.

Backstroke Brenda is in lane 6
So 6 x 6 is 36.

Cycling Susie is going for her fastest time
7 lots of 7 are 49.

Triple Jump Tracey's feet are very sore
8 groups of 8 equal 64.

Shot Put Tony is having so much fun
9 x 9 is 81.

Long Jump Jim how fast he sped
'Cause 10 x 10 is 100.

High Dive Clive's
Mixed times table challenge
(2, 4, 5, 10 time tables)

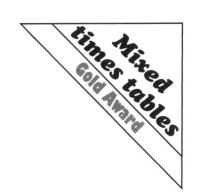

Mixed times tables
Gold Award

1 x 2 =	10 ÷ 2 =	7 x 2 =	2 x 4 =	
10 x 12 =	2 x 5 =		5 x 9 =	9 x 4 =
9 x 2 =		20 ÷ 2 =	8 x 2 =	
10 ÷ 5 =	1 x 10 =		5 x 7 =	24 ÷ 4 =
		2 x 2 =	5 x 5 =	2 x 12 =
3 x 5 =	90 ÷ 10 =		1 x 5 =	
	10 x 5 =	4 x 4 =	16 ÷ 4 =	6 x 5 =
1 x 4 =			6 x 2 =	
	5 x 10 =	20 ÷ 5 =		7 x 4 =
3 x 2 =		9 x 5 =	8 x 4 =	50 ÷ 10 =
4 x 11 =	8 ÷ 2 =	3 x 10 =	60 ÷ 10 =	
8 x 5 =	6 x 10 =	6 x 4 =		4 x 2 =
45 ÷ 5 =	5 x 2 =		80 ÷ 10 =	15 ÷ 5 =
5 x 4 =		4 x 10 =	40 ÷ 10 =	36 ÷ 4 =
	8 ÷ 4 =	14 ÷ 2 =	8 x 10 =	
7 x 10 =	4 x 3 =	10 x 7 =		16 ÷ 2 =
20 ÷ 4 =		30 ÷ 5 =	9 x 10 =	60 ÷ 5 =

High Dive Clive's Mixed times table word problem challenge
(2, 4, 5, 10 time tables)

1. Everybody who comes to watch the races spends £2 each on ice-cream and drinks. How much money would 9 people spend?

2. There are 50 swimmers in total. If there are 5 swimming races, how many swimmers compete in each race?

3. There are 4 types of energy sweets for sale. I sell 7 of each type. How many have I sold altogether?

4. 10 people enter each of the 8 swimming events. How many people is that altogether?

5. There are 5 people in a relay race. They each run 2 laps. How many laps is that altogether?

High Dive Clive's
Badges

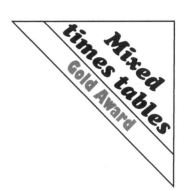

High Dive Clive's
Character mask

Colour in your character mask. Then cut out and stick to a band of card, ready to place around your head.

Triathlon Saffron's Mixed times table challenge

(3, 6, 7, 8, 9 time tables)

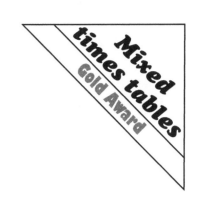

1 x 3 =	3 x 3 =	1 x 9 =	1 x 6 =	6 x 12 =
4 x 6 =	4 x 8 =	2 x 7 =		5 x 8 =
5 x 9 =		49 ÷ 7 =	2 x 3 =	
7 x 7 =	36 ÷ 6 =		63 ÷ 7 =	6 x 6 =
	33 ÷ 3 =	4 x 3 =	10 x 9 =	24 ÷ 3 =
2 x 6 =	3 x 7 =		3 x 8 =	
	10 x 8 =	7 x 9 =	5 x 6 =	8 x 8 =
8 x 6 =			42 ÷ 6 =	
72 ÷ 8 =	81 ÷ 9 =	7 x 3 =		5 x 7 =
2 x 8 =	28 ÷ 7 =	10 x 7 =	12 ÷ 6 =	36 ÷ 9 =
	14 ÷ 7 =	27 ÷ 9 =	7 x 6 =	
4 x 7 =	18 ÷ 3 =	6 x 7 =		6 x 9 =
9 x 7 =	7 x 8 =	56 ÷ 8 =	18 ÷ 6 =	9 x 3 =
88 ÷ 8 =		3 x 9 =	10 x 3 =	12 ÷ 3 =
	2 x 9 =	5 x 3 =	9 x 8 =	
54 ÷ 6 =	4 x 9 =			1 x 8 =
8 x 7 =	1 x 7 =	3 x 6 =	45 ÷ 9 =	10 x 6 =
18 ÷ 9 =		9 x 6 =	9 x 9 =	8 x 9 =

Triathlon Saffron's Mixed times table word problem challenge

(3, 6, 7, 8, 9 time tables)

1. Triathlon Saffron is organizing some races. If there is a bronze, silver and gold award in each of the 9 races, how many awards in total does she need to order?

2. There are 36 runners across 6 events. Each race has the same number of runners. How many runners are in each event?

3. There are 7 different types of sports drink. She sells 9 of each type. How many sports drinks did she sell in total?

4. There are 9 events in a day and each event takes 8 minutes. How many minutes altogether does the day of events take?

5. There are 8 people in each of 7 events. How many people are there altogether?

Triathlon Saffron's Badges

Mixed times tables
Gold Award

Triathlon Saffron's
Character mask

Mixed
times tables
Gold Award✓✓

Colour in your character mask. Then cut out and stick to a band of card, ready to place around your head.

Mighty Multiples
Gold Award

Congratulations!

Awarded to

_____

On

_____

You have successfully completed the following awards:

High Jump
Heather

Backstroke
Brenda

Cycling
Susie

Triple Jump
Tracey

Shot Put
Tony

High Dive
Clive

Triathlon
Saffron

1000m Glenda's 11 times table activities

1	×	11	=	11
2	×	11	=	22
3	×	11	=	33
4	×	11	=	44
5	×	11	=	55
6	×	11	=	66
7	×	11	=	77
8	×	11	=	88
9	×	11	=	99
10	×	11	=	110
11	×	11	=	121
12	×	11	=	132

Have a relay race with 12 people in each team. Every time you hand the baton over, the team member taking the baton has to say the next 11x answer.

Label 12 balls 1 to 12. Put them in a basket. Take turns at running to the basket and selecting a ball. For each ball you select, you have to multiply it by 11.

Do laps of your garden counting in 11s. You can't stop until you get to 11 x 12. Who can complete the tables in the fewest laps?

Spread number cards (1–12) around a space. Player 1 runs to grab a number and takes it back to the Player 2. If Player 2 can times it by 11 correctly, they can keep it. If they get it wrong Player 1 has to put it back. Keep taking turns until all the numbers are gone. The player with the most numbers wins.

1000m Glenda's
11 times table

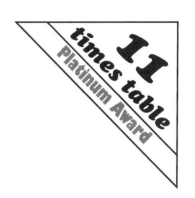

1	×	**11**	=	11
2	×	**11**	=	22
3	×	**11**	=	33
4	×	**11**	=	44
5	×	**11**	=	55
6	×	**11**	=	66
7	×	**11**	=	77
8	×	**11**	=	88
9	×	**11**	=	99
10	×	**11**	=	110
11	×	**11**	=	121
12	×	**11**	=	132

1000m Glenda's
Number fans

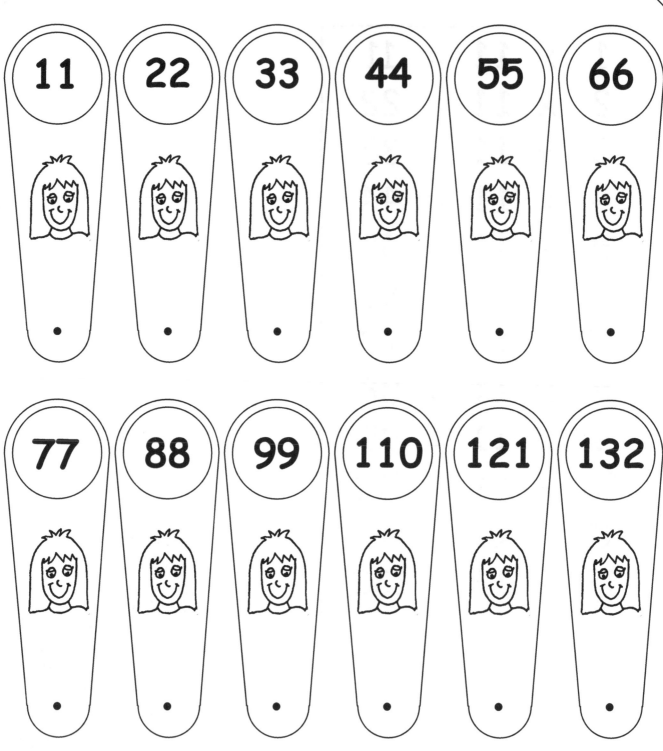

1000m Glenda's
Visual grouping

11 × _____ = _____

For example:
11 x 2 = 22   2 squares

1000m Glenda's Badges

1000m Glenda's
Character mask

Colour in your character mask. Then cut out and stick to a band of card, ready to place around your head.

1000m Glenda's
11 times table poem

1000m Glenda doesn't take it steady or slow
1 x 11 is 11, she definitely knows!

When she first started running, she hadn't a clue
2 x 11 is 22.

She put in a lot of training, whenever she was free
3 x 11 is 33.

As she started improving, she won more and more
4 x 11 is 44.

With every win, she gets a high five
5 x 11 is 55.

She likes to give her tactics a mix
6 x 11 is 66.

She knows that's the way to winning heaven
7 x 11 is 77.

She's always sharing tips with her mates
8 x 11 is 88.

In training she yells, 'That trophy's mine'
9 x 11 that's 99.

Glenda loves to be in the winning pen!
10 x 11 that's 110!

She never gives up until she's won,
11 x 11 is 121.

Over the line, in first place, she flew
11 x 12 is 132.

1000m Glenda's
11 times table song

Tracks
26 & 39

Chorus
1000m Glenda is running round the track,
Sings her 11 times table with every single lap.

1 x 11 that's 11
Glenda's vest is number seven
2 x 11 is 22
Wow, watch Glenda, that lap she really flew!

1000m Glenda chorus

11 x 3 that's 33
Glenda is so fast, you see
4 x 11 that's 44,
Come on Glenda, there's not much more!

1000m Glenda chorus

5 x 11 equals 55
She runs to the line, then she'll dive
11 x 6 is 66,
Come on Glenda quick, quick, quick!

1000m Glenda chorus

11 x 7 that's 77
Oh watch Glenda she's in running heaven
8 x 11 makes 88
Oh Glenda you are so great!

1000m Glenda chorus

9 x 11 is 99,
Glenda's nearly over the line
10 x 11 that's 110
Oh look at Glenda, she's done it again!

1000m Glenda chorus

11 x 11 is 121,
Glenda's so proud that she's won!
12 x 11 makes 132
Oh look at Glenda, she's smiling too!

1000m Glenda chorus x 2

Sung to the tune of 'Twinkle, twinkle little star'.

1000m Glenda's 11 times table challenge

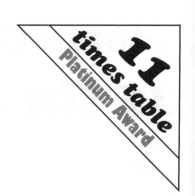

3 x 11 =	11 x 6 =	1 x 11 =	11 ÷ 1 =	11 x 5 =
	11 x 2 =		8 x 11 =	9 x 11 =
11 x 4 =		5 x 11 =		
55 ÷ 11 =	11 x 3 =		6 x 11 =	11 x 11 =
	88 ÷ 11 =	33 ÷ 11 =		121 ÷ 11 =
7 x 11 =	11 x 7 =	99 ÷ 11 =	11 x 10 =	4 x 11 =
110 ÷ 11 =		66 ÷ 11 =	11 x 1 =	11 ÷ 11 =
	5 x 11 =	12 x 11 =		132 ÷ 11 =
11 x 12 =			44 ÷ 11 =	
10 x 11 =	11 x 8 =	77 ÷ 11 =	2 x 11 =	11 x 9 =

1000m Glenda's 11 times table word problem challenge

1. Glenda is getting ready for her race. She needs 11 energy sweets 4 times a day on the day of her race. How many energy sweets does she have in total on a race day?

2. 11 people are in Glenda's race and they all run 7 laps. How many laps is that altogether?

3. As a professional runner Glenda is sponsored by a bottled water company. They donate 121 bottles of water to Glenda, she shares these equally between herself and her 10 team mates. How many bottles do they have each?

4. Each of the 9 athletes in Glenda's team have 11 pairs of trainers. How many pairs of shoes are there in the team show store?

5. 1000m Glenda runs 11 laps. For each lap she gets 8 points. How many points does she gain in total?

Aerobic Alan's 12 *times table* activities

1	×	**12**	=	12
2	×	**12**	=	24
3	×	**12**	=	36
4	×	**12**	=	48
5	×	**12**	=	60
6	×	**12**	=	72
7	×	**12**	=	84
8	×	**12**	=	96
9	×	**12**	=	108
10	×	**12**	=	120
11	×	**12**	=	132
12	×	**12**	=	144

Set up 4 aerobic activities. Race your partner: you must keep doing each activity until you have said your 12 times table. Who can complete all 4 activities first?

Choose a partner – one takes star jumps and the other takes press ups. Race each other to see who can do more of their exercise whilst counting in 12s. Swap over. Can you beat your partner's record?

Have times table questions on cards. Work with a partner and answer using your bodies to make the number shapes.

How many press ups can you do before counting to 144 in 12s? Do it again and see if you can beat that!

Aerobic Alan's
12 times table

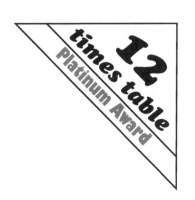

1	×	**12**	=	12
2	×	**12**	=	24
3	×	**12**	=	36
4	×	**12**	=	48
5	×	**12**	=	60
6	×	**12**	=	72
7	×	**12**	=	84
8	×	**12**	=	96
9	×	**12**	=	108
10	×	**12**	=	120
11	×	**12**	=	132
12	×	**12**	=	144

Aerobic Alan's
Number fans

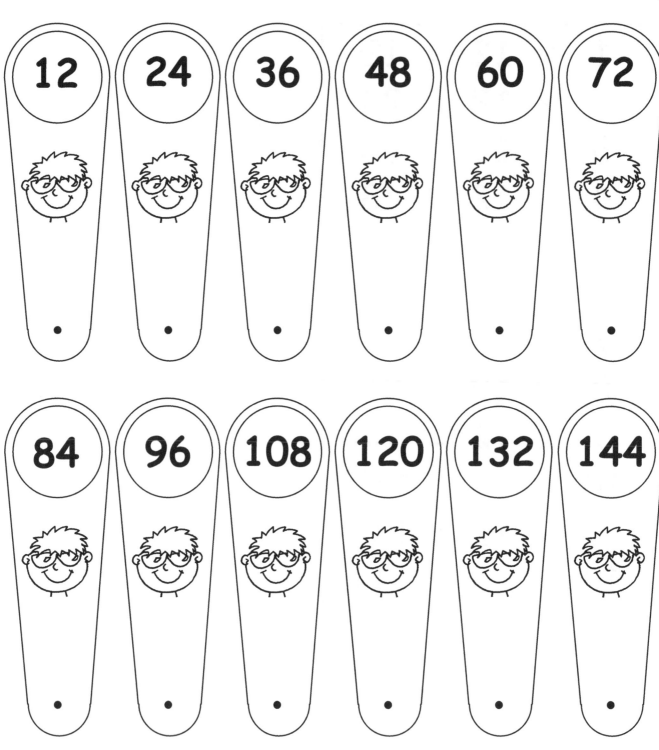

12   24   36   48   60   72

84   96   108   120   132   144

Aerobic Alan's
Visual grouping

12 × ___ = _____

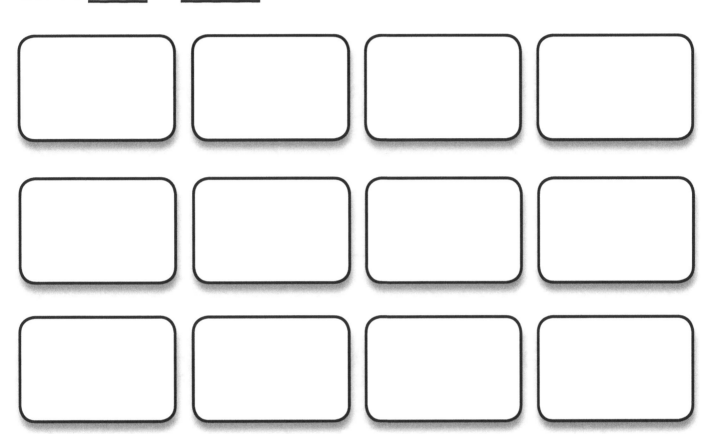

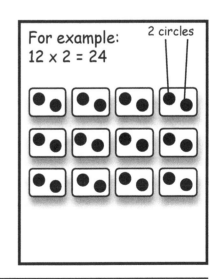

For example:
12 × 2 = 24   2 circles

Aerobic Alan's
Badges

12 times table
Platinum Award

Aerobic Alan's
Character mask

Colour in your character mask. Then cut out and stick to a band of card, ready to place around your head.

Aerobic Alan's
12 times table poem

Aerobic Alan has the room in a whirl
1 x 12 is 12.

He is up and down, across on the floor
Always remembering 2 x 12 is 24.

His aerobic workouts are a real mix
3 x 12 equals 36.

Beginners like to attend with a mate
4 x 12 is 48.

The experts think they're really nifty
5 x 12 that's 60.

It really doesn't matter if you haven't a clue
6 x 12 is 72.

He'll have you jumping up and down on the floor
7 x 12 equals 84.

Running around quick, quick, quick
8 x 12 is 96.

With hundreds of moves you must not be late
9 x 12 is 108.

Shimmy to the left – that is plenty
10 x 12 is 120.

Star jumps he has you doing too.
11 x 12 makes 132.

It's time for a rest so lie on the floor!
12 x 12 is 144 !

Aerobic Alan's
12 times table song

Tracks
27 & 40

Aerobic Alan is really great
At learning the 12 times table.
He can move and jump and shout
Like nobody else is able.

1 x 12 is 12 he says
Learning your 12s is easy.
2 x 12 is 24
See this is lemon squeezy.

12 x 3 is 36
Aerobic Alan will help you get fit!
4 x 12 is 48
Don't forget to bring your mates.

5 x 12 is 60
Alan is really fast on his feet
6 x 12 is 72
Aerobic Alan will show you the moves.

12 x 7 is 84
He'll have you doing sit-ups on the floor.
8 x 12 is 96
Come on move, quick, quick, quick.

9 x 12's 108
Alan's moves are just so great
10 x 12 is 120
Steady does it, you've done plenty!

11 x 12 is 132
It's just hard if only you knew!
12 x 12's 144
Everyone's screaming for some more

Aerobic Alan is just so great
He makes the 12s so easy!
He can move and jump and shout
Like nobody else is able.

Aerobic Alan is just so great
He makes the 12s so easy!
He can move and jump and shout
Like nobody else is able.

Sung to the tune of 'Jack and Jill'.

Aerobic Alan's
12 times table challenge

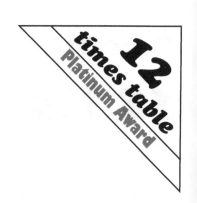

1 x 12 =		12 x 12 =	96 ÷ 12 =	12 ÷ 1 =
	3 x 12 =	108 ÷ 12 =		2 x 12 =
24 ÷ 12 =		12 x 9 =	4 x 12 =	
72 ÷ 12 =	12 x 7 =	6 x 12 =		12 x 6 =
5 x 12 =			144 ÷ 12 =	60 ÷ 12 =
12 x 5 =	12 x 8 =	12 x 3 =		
	12 ÷ 12 =		12 x 4 =	10 x 12 =
12 ÷ 12 =		36 ÷ 12 =	8 x 12 =	
7 x 12 =	12 x 10 =	9 x 12 =		48 ÷ 12 =
132 ÷ 12 =	12 x 1 =	84 ÷ 12 =	11 x 12 =	12 x 11 =

Aerobic Alan's 12 times table word problem challenge

1. Aerobic Alan has 144 weights to move to another gym. He has 12 days to do so. How many weights must he move a day, in order to move them all equally?

2. Aerobic Alan has 12 people attending his aerobics class that night. Each person needs 2 bottles of water and 2 energy bars. How many items altogether will Aerobic Alan need to buy at the shops to have enough for everyone?

3. In his aerobic routine Alan does 12 star jumps, 12 squats, 12 kicks and 12 sit ups. How many moves is that in total?

4. Aerobic Alan takes 12 minutes to do one routine. How many minutes would 8 routines take?

5. Everyone that attends Aerobic Alan's classes must have their own sweatband. Alan is off to buy these! He has 9 classes and 12 people attend each class. How many sweat bands must he buy?

Mighty Multiples

Platinum Award

Congratulations!

Awarded to

_____

On

_____

You have successfully completed the following awards:

1000m
Glenda

Aerobic
Alan

Mighty Multiples' 144 grid

1	2	3	4	5	6	7	8	9	10	11	12
2	4	6	8	10	12	14	16	18	20	22	24
3	6	9	12	15	18	21	24	27	30	33	36
4	8	12	16	20	24	28	32	36	40	44	48
5	10	15	20	25	30	35	40	45	50	55	60
6	12	18	24	30	36	42	48	54	60	66	72
7	14	21	28	35	42	49	56	63	70	77	84
8	16	24	32	40	48	56	64	72	80	88	96
9	18	27	36	45	54	63	72	81	90	99	108
10	20	30	40	50	60	70	80	90	100	110	120
11	22	33	44	55	66	77	88	99	110	121	132
12	24	36	48	60	72	84	96	108	120	132	144

Mighty Multiples' blank bingo grid
(8 numbers)

Mighty Multiples' blank bingo grid
(6 numbers)

Mighty Multiples' number fans

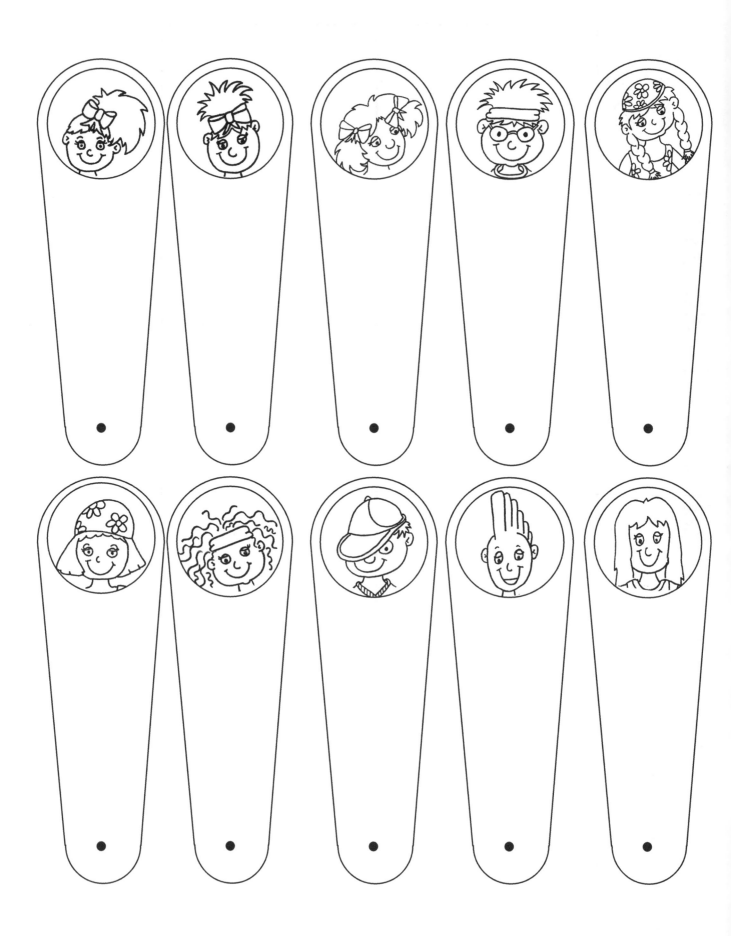

Mighty Multiples' number fans

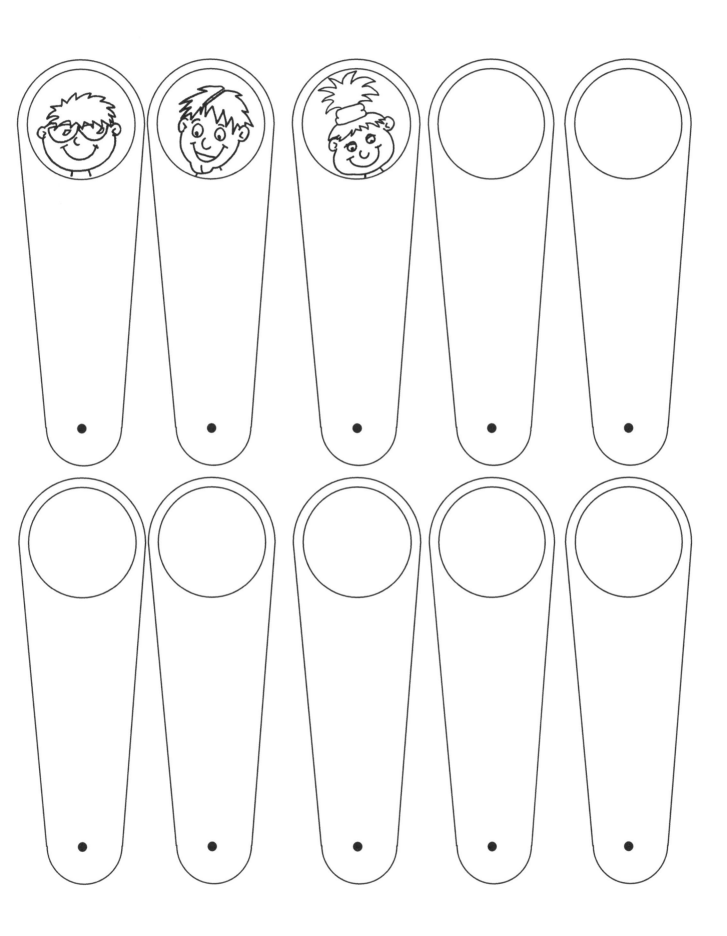

Mighty Multiples' number fans

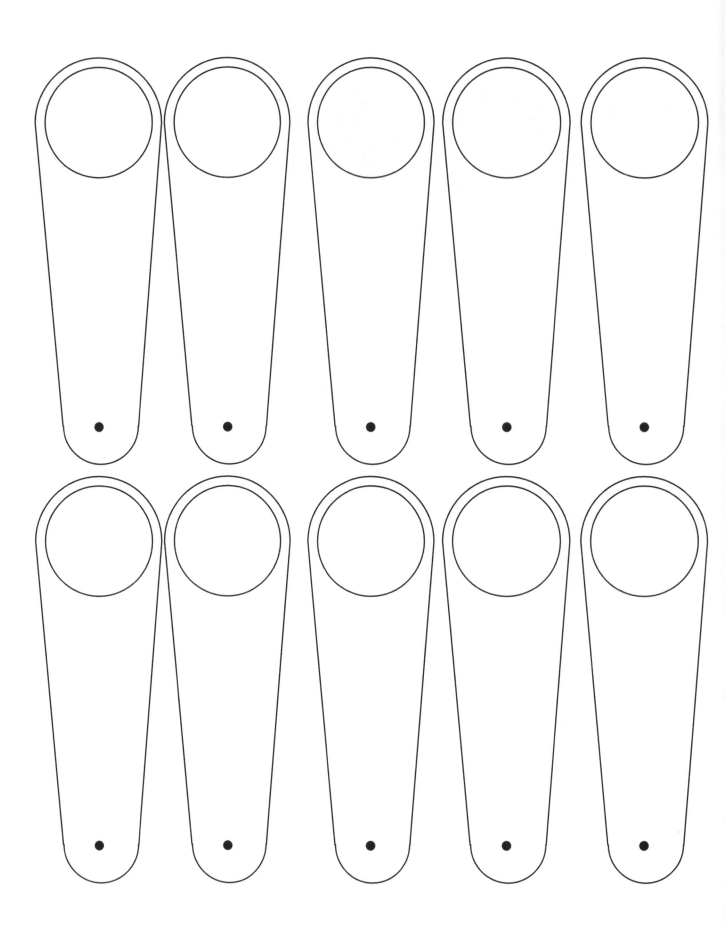

Contents of CDs

Track no.	Track title	Page in book
CD1: 1	Mighty Multiples poem	10
2	100m Peter's number stories poem	38
3	200m Travis's number bonds poem	48
4	400m Sinitta's 2 times table poem	59
5	Long Jump Jim's 10 times table poem	69
6	Javelin John's 5 times table poem	79
7	Freestyle Freda's 4 times table poem	89
8	High Jump Heather's 3 times table poem	100
9	Backstroke Brenda's 6 times table poem	110
10	Cycling Susie's 7 times table poem	120
11	Triple Jump Tracey's 8 times table poem	130
12	Shot Put Tony's 9 times table poem	140
13	1000m Glenda's 11 times table poem	160
14	Aerobic Alan's 12 times table poem	170
15	100m Peter's number stories song	39
16	200m Travis's number bonds song	49
17	400m Sinitta's 2 times table song	60
18	Long Jump Jim's 10 times table song	70
19	Javelin John's 5 times table song	80
20	Freestyle Freda's 4 times table song	90
21	High Jump Heather's 3 times table song	101
22	Backstroke Brenda's 6 times table song	111
23	Cycling Susie's 7 times table song	121
24	Triple Jump Tracey's 8 times table song	131
25	Shot Put Tony's 9 times table song	141
26	1000m Glenda's 11 times table song	161
27	Aerobic Alan's 12 times table song	171
CD2: 28	100m Peter's number stories song (instrumental version)	39
29	200m Travis's number bonds song (instrumental version)	49
30	400m Sinitta's 2 times table song (instrumental version)	60
31	Long Jump Jim's 10 times table song (instrumental version)	70
32	Javelin John's 5 times table song (instrumental version)	80
33	Freestyle Freda's 4 times table song (instrumental version)	90
34	High Jump Heather's 3 times table song (instrumental version)	101
35	Backstroke Brenda's 6 times table song (instrumental version)	111
36	Cycling Susie's 7 times table song (instrumental version)	121
37	Triple Jump Tracey's 8 times table song (instrumental version)	131
38	Shot Put Tony's 9 times table song (instrumental version)	141
39	1000m Glenda's 11 times table song (instrumental version)	161
40	Aerobic Alan's 12 times table song (instrumental version)	171

Lightning Source UK Ltd.
Milton Keynes UK
UKOW07f0618030216

267651UK00003B/28/P